Virus
in
the Cell

SCIENCE FOR EVERYMAN

2571

Virus
in
the Cell

J. GORDON COOK

FELLOW OF THE ROYAL INSTITUTE OF CHEMISTS

THE DIAL PRESS   1957   NEW YORK

To RICHARD

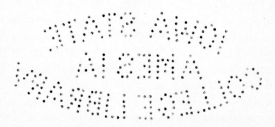

Preface

THE treatment of disease has made more progress during
the last half-century than it did in the previous 500 years.
We have now grown accustomed to being able to destroy
disease germs as they seek to invade the human body;
sulphonamides and other synthetic drugs, penicillin, aureomycin, and the antibiotics have given us weapons against
the germ such as we have never had before. But in spite of
the revolution that these drugs have caused, we still have
nothing that we can use against the special sort of germ
we call the virus.

Viruses are responsible for many of the most intractable
human diseases; poliomyelitis and influenza, smallpox, yellow fever, and the common cold are virus diseases. Almost
every species of living thing is subject to virus attack;
viruses cause foot-and-mouth disease in cattle and distemper in dogs, psittacosis in parrots and flacherie in silkworms, curly top in sugar beet and leaf-roll in potatoes.

The virus, through its persistent attack on all forms of
life, has become of immense economic and social significance in our modern world. But this tiny germ is also
intriguing on its own account; it differs fundamentally
from the 'ordinary' germs that we regard as independent
living things.

Viruses are so small that we cannot see them through
the optical microscope. They do not 'live' in the sense
that bacteria do. Away from its 'host' the virus is a particle
of chemical substance; many viruses are crystalline and

show no more sign of life than a crystal of common salt. Yet, once it has entered the living cells of its host, the virus can 'come alive.' It multiplies, and produces others of its kind.

In this respect the virus provides us with a link between the world of life and the world of inanimate 'mineral' things. Virus research is leading us towards an understanding of the chemical processes that are the basis of life itself.

I should like to acknowledge with thanks the very great help I have received from Dr Christopher Andrewes, of the National Institute for Medical Research, Mill Hill, London, N.W.7.

J.G.C.

Contents

Illustrations

1

The Invisible Germ

SCIENCE is carrying us into the future with bewildering speed. We have learned how to liberate atomic energy. We can look forward to visiting the moon by rocket-ship. We can fight disease with penicillin and aureomycin, and massacre insects with DDT. We are turning coal into clothes, and petrol into synthetic soaps. But there is one great stronghold of nature on which we have as yet made little impression. We are still unable to explain or duplicate the phenomenon of life itself.

As an unsolved mystery, life remains a fascinating problem for the scientist. And the more we discover of living processes in terms of chemical equations, the more inexplicable the ultimate life-force becomes.

During the last few years science has been attacking this problem from many different angles. Biology and chemistry, physics and medicine, have met and intermingled in this great struggle to understand the meaning of life. In the midst of it all we are finding that our investigation is centring more and more around one aspect of research—the nature and behaviour of the tiny invisible germs we describe as viruses.

These viruses, which are the cause of many plant and animal diseases (including human diseases such as poliomyelitis and influenza), have become a connecting link between the world of the living and the non-living. And we are finding in the virus an effective point at which to concentrate our researches into life itself.

It is strange that in the minds of most of us the distinction between the living and the non-living should be sharp and crystal-clear. "Animal and vegetable" lie on one side of the barrier of life; "mineral" occupies the other. And never the twain shall meet.

A cat is living; the saucer from which it drinks is non-living. The idea of any sort of intermediate stage seems quite preposterous. So we think, until we *really* start to think.

What are the characteristics of a living thing? How do we recognize life in something, so that we can classify it as being on one side or the other of the barrier?

To start with, a living thing can usually grow and move. We also expect it to have some sort of respiratory activity. And, of course, it is able to reproduce in some way so as to perpetuate its species. These are phenomena we associate with living things. But all living things do not necessarily exhibit all these characteristics. Nor are they all absent in the case of some non-living things.

The fact that you are reading this book is enough to indicate that you are alive. You are a living organism, capable of a sustained and independent existence. But it is not easy to say, from this point of view, whether individual parts of you are alive or not. If your appendix is taken out you will continue to live even though some part of your body has been removed. You are undoubtedly still to be regarded as a living thing. But what about the appendix? The tissue forming it can be maintained in a ' living ' state if it is bathed in appropriate fluids.

In the same way isolated hearts can go on pumping blood even though they are no longer part of the body. Roots of plants have been kept growing for years after being severed from the plant itself.

These things are certainly not inanimate. But they cannot reproduce themselves in the sense that normal living things do. Are they then ' alive '?

Considered from the other side of the borderline between life and no-life, the problem remains the same. The salt you sprinkle on your dinner is a mineral substance. It is inanimate, and we would never dream of classing it as a living thing. Yet in a sense it can reproduce; a crystal of salt in a brine solution will grow to a larger size of crystal with a similar shape. New crystals, all related one to another in general form, will appear as though from ' seed ' inside the brine.

So life and the absence of life become extremely difficult to define as we examine them in detail. The idea of a borderline case becomes more acceptable as we think more deeply on the problem; something which under certain circumstances can ' live ' and yet under other circumstances is inanimate.

It is in this strange No Man's Land of Life that we find the virus. This tiny germ, so small that we cannot see it even through the most powerful optical microscope, is in some respects alive. It can multiply and reproduce. Yet at the same time it can behave as ordinary ' mineral ' matter, with no more signs of life than the proverbial door-nail.

Viruses have become a link that joins our two worlds together. And in their study we are finding a most effective approach to the fundamental processes of life itself.

It is astonishing to remember that less than a century has passed since Louis Pasteur and Robert Koch established the idea of microbes as the cause of infectious disease. At the time of the Great Exhibition, in 1851, doctors were still in the dark about the nature of disease. Epidemics of typhoid fever were believed to be spread by the bad smells seeping from open drains. Malaria was caused by mysterious vapours that floated up from swampy ground or could be attributed even more vaguely to an Act of God. Superstition and legend were the background against which medicine had to operate.

The germ theory rationalized medicine in a fashion as startling as the Atomic Theory had reorganized science at the beginning of the century. Doctors began to fight disease by attacking the germs that caused it. Bacteriology became a science, and the microscope revealed the secrets of the germs that brought innumerable diseases.

Germs were isolated from infected patients and grown on suitable broths in the laboratory. It became possible to study the characteristics of the different germs, and we began to understand how to deal with them when they got into the human body.

At first, the enthusiasts believed that in their living germs they had the solution to all human and animal diseases. But as the study of germs progressed it became apparent that there were many infectious diseases of which no visible germ could be identified as the cause.

Pasteur himself recognized the limitations of the germ theory. Diseases like smallpox, for example, were all too obviously infectious. But no smallpox germ could be detected in the blood of the victim.

Pasteur searched for the germ that caused rabies, but he could find nothing. He suggested as an explanation that the germs of these mystery diseases might be too small to be seen even with the help of the microscope. As it has since turned out, he had hit upon the truth. He had guessed at the existence of the viruses.

As medicine and bacteriology developed with the acceptance of the idea of germs the mystery of the virus diseases deepened. It was difficult to prove the existence of germs so small that they could not be seen. It was impossible to study something that existed only as an idea.

In 1892 the first real evidence in support of the virus was found. By that time scientists had discovered that they could strain out even the smallest germs from a liquid by using special filters. One germ-filter of this sort was made from a very fine compressed earth called Kieselguhr. Liquid forced through a Kieselguhr filter was free of germs when examined under the microscope.

In 1892 a Russian botanist, Dmitrii Iwanowski, was experimenting with a disease of the tobacco plant. This disease attacked the plant and caused a mosaic-like mottling on the leaves. Its name—tobacco mosaic disease—has now become familiar to every virus worker in the world.

Iwanowski filtered some of the juice from diseased tobacco plants through a germ-filter. He found that the clear liquid which came through was entirely free of visible germs. And yet, when he injected this filtered juice into a healthy tobacco plant, it developed mosaic disease.

Here, for the first time, was direct evidence that some sort of germ existed which was too small to be seen under the microscope. It confirmed Pasteur's suggestion of invisible germs and was the starting point for modern virus research.

Since Iwanowski's experiments the investigation of viruses has increased steadily in intensity and importance. The name given to the invisible germs was a sign of our ignorance of their nature. Virus means "a poison." Viruses were something unidentified which caused disease.

Into the virus class went many of the diseases for which no germ had been identified. Soon after Iwanowski's experiment scientists found that foot-and-mouth disease, the disease which is still costing the world millions of pounds a year in slaughtered cattle, was a virus disease. It was caused by a germ so small that it passed through the normal filter.

In 1900 yellow fever was shown to be transmitted by the mosquito. And yet no germ could be detected in the insect or the patient. It was a virus disease.

So, gradually, by the turn of the century the conception of invisible germs, or viruses, was becoming accepted. Where plants or animals or human beings were suffering from diseases which could be transmitted, and yet which had no identifiable germ—these were explained as virus diseases. The viruses themselves remained a complete mystery. Scientists were certain they were there, floating about in the blood of animals or in the sap of plants. But there was no proof. Nobody had ever seen a virus.

For forty years after Iwanowski's experiment with his tobacco plants the virus mystery went unsolved. More and more diseases were put down as virus diseases. Many of the most troublesome human diseases were recognized as being caused by the invisible germs. Influenza, poliomyelitis, smallpox, measles, mumps, the common cold—some of these were among the most infectious of all our diseases. But we remained in the dark as to the shape and form of the germ responsible in every case.

To a scientist, a mystery like this is always a challenge to be met. Viruses were of vital importance. Yet we knew nothing about them. The experimental effort therefore increased steadily as scientists turned their attention to them. But virus research bristles with difficulties, and progress was inevitably slow. Viruses could not be seen at all, and in this respect research was carried out entirely in the dark. Many viruses are remarkably infectious, and the diseases they cause in human beings are often dangerous. Great care had to be taken in laboratories where virus research was being carried out.

The most difficult problem of all was raised by the absolute refusal of the virus to reproduce in laboratory apparatus. Viruses differed from the normal visible bacteria. Ordinary germs, such as those that cause cholera or tuberculosis, can be cultivated on appropriate food in a test-tube. Bacteria behave like tiny plants growing in a midget garden; left on the surface of a jelly that contains a supply of suitable food, they will multiply and develop into colonies. Though the individual bacteria are too small to be seen with the naked eye, they will form colonies containing millions of descendants, which can be seen as tiny patches on the surface of the jelly.

This independence of the normal bacterium enables the scientist to provide himself with ample specimens for research. All he does is to put a few bacteria on to a jellified broth in a test-tube, and then warm the test-tube in an incubator. Kept at body-heat, germs that cause a typical disease will multiply as though they were living inside the human body.

But viruses would not grow in this way. Outside the 'host'—the animal or plant in which they caused disease—viruses refused to multiply no matter how carefully they were treated. Virus scientists were unable to provide themselves with supplies of the germs they could not see.

By the early 1930's science was becoming baffled and frustrated by the virus. Without any doubt organisms of some sort were able to pass infection from one living thing to another. But nobody had seen them; nor could anybody persuade these hypothetical viruses to reproduce in the way that other living things do. Was it possible then that viruses were something of a myth? Could it be that they were not living things at all?

Faced with these problems, scientists began to think along new lines. Perhaps viruses were, after all, simply chemicals of some sort which caused disease inside the plant or animal?

This new conception changed the methods of attack on the viruses. It could not account for the infectiousness of virus disease and the apparent multiplication of the viruses inside their host. But anything was worth trying. Instead of hunting for an invisible micro-organism, scientists began to try and isolate the viruses from plant juices and animal blood as though they were ordinary chemicals dissolved in the liquid.

Very soon, during the early 1930's, the new line of attack began to give results. The virus chosen for study during many of these experiments was once again the tobacco mosaic virus that had been studied by Iwanowski nearly half a century before.

In 1935 the first real success was announced in the intensified attack on viruses. Dr W. M. Stanley, an American scientist, separated a solid substance from the sap of infected tobacco plants and suggested that this was in fact the virus of tobacco mosaic disease.

The pure virus—if such it was—turned out to be a beautiful crystalline solid in the form of long, thin needles.

Here was a strange situation indeed. A virus had been concentrated and purified and appeared to have the superficial characteristics of an ordinary chemical. The tiny individual particles that float in the sap of the infected tobacco plant must be able to align themselves with geometric precision into the regular ranks that build up into crystals. The tobacco mosaic virus had, therefore, much in common with inanimate crystalline chemicals such as salt or sugar.

In spite of their apparent 'mineral' character, these virus crystals retained the ability to infect a plant with mosaic disease. Rubbed over the leaves of a tobacco plant, the crystals caused disease. The virus particles forming the crystals appeared to be able to increase and multiply inside the infected plant, like any ordinary living germ. They possessed the essential characteristic of life itself—the power of reproduction.

Since 1935 other viruses have been isolated and purified, and wonderful techniques have been devised for separating infinitesimal amounts of virus from large volumes of infected sap and animal fluids. Dr Stanley was awarded the Nobel Prize for his achievements, which opened the way to our modern understanding of the nature of the virus particle.

Many plant viruses, like the tobacco mosaic virus, have been obtained as crystalline substances. Only one animal virus, the poliomyelitis virus, has been isolated in this characteristic 'chemical' form.

These virus chemicals have all been shown to possess the power of infection inherent in the sap or serum from which they have been concentrated. Some scientists believed that the crystals were merely contaminated with the actual living germ. But experiments have proved that this cannot be so. The virus chemicals are in fact the disease-producing agents.

The isolation of viruses in crystalline form enables us to see them in the sense that we see enormous numbers of individual particles crammed together. But it does not help us in our efforts to make out what the virus particle itself looks like. The virus crystal can be compared to the colony of bacteria on the surface of a layer of broth; we can see the colony with the naked eye, but we cannot see what the individual bacteria are like. To do this we must study a small part of the colony under the microscope.

In the case of the virus the individual particles are so small that we cannot see them through the ordinary microscope. Optical microscopes are limited in their power of magnification by the wave-lengths of the visible light they use. Most viruses are so much smaller than the wavelengths of the light that the light flows past them with as little concern as the ocean swell rolling past a stick protruding from the sea.

One or two of the largest viruses can, in fact, affect the rays of visible light; it is possible, for example, to see a stained smallpox virus as a tiny dot under a first-class optical microscope. But no details of its structure can be seen.

In order to increase the seeing-power of a microscope so that it can penetrate into the world of viruses we have to decrease the wave-length of the light that is used.

During the 1920's microscopes were devised which used short-wave, ultra-violet light instead of ordinary, visible light. Ultra-violet light does not affect the retina of the human eye in the way that visible light rays do; we cannot therefore 'see' the specimen directly in an ultra-violet microscope. But ultra-violet light will affect the emulsion on a photographic plate in the same way as ordinary light. And we can photograph an object in a microscope that uses ultra-violet light.

With the help of this instrument photographs of some of the larger viruses were obtained. But ultra-violet light extended the range of the microscope by only a limited amount. It did not take us far enough into the micro-world of viruses to provide a real picture of these extraordinary particles.

During the 1930's the science of electronics made fast progress. Streams of electrons were shown to behave in many respects like waves of radiation of very small wavelength. And physicists realized that it might be possible to use electron-streams instead of light to reach into an entirely new world of ultra-microscopy.

Electron-streams can be regarded as waves only one-hundred-thousandth of the length of waves of visible light. They can be focused with the help of electro-magnets, just as light rays are focused through lenses. And although they cannot be seen directly with the naked eye, electron-beams can expose a photographic plate or make a fluorescent screen glow with light.

Shortly before World War II microscopes had been built in which electrons did the work that had previously been done by visible light. By 1938 photographs of individual virus particles had been taken.

Since then the electron microscope has made immense progress and we can now 'see' things only a millionth of an inch in diameter. With the help of this astonishing instrument we have been able to photograph many plant and animal viruses. Some, like the tobacco mosaic virus, are little rod-shaped particles. Others, like the influenza virus, resemble tiny puff-balls.

So, at last, virus research is going ahead with the enemy clearly in view. We know what many viruses look like. We can persuade millions of the individual particles to collect together into clumps, often crystalline, which are large enough to be handled like ordinary chemicals. We can purify some of these virus chemicals and analyse them just as though they were vitamins or drugs or other inanimate chemical substances.

This sort of fundamental virus research is in its infancy to-day. Although we can treat these disease-producing substances as chemicals and subject them to normal scientific investigation, they are difficult subjects for study.

Yet this virus research is stimulating work. The prospects are exciting. For at the back of our minds, as we probe the mysteries of the virus, we know that we are exploring on the boundary land that separates the world of life from the world of inanimate mineral things. These crystalline chemicals, formed from millions of virus particles, will 'come alive' inside a living cell.

2

Smallpox and Vaccination

ONE fascinating result of the study of archæological remains is that it has shown us how long we have been suffering from some of our diseases. Smallpox is a good example.

This terrible disease, which is still bringing death and disfigurement to thousands of people in many parts of the world every year, has been with us since the earliest days of civilization. The characteristic scars of smallpox have been found on the skin of Egyptian mummies of the Twentieth Dynasty.

Smallpox was probably introduced into Western Europe from India and Asia during the Crusades in the eleventh century. It has remained with us ever since, and although it has been virtually stamped out in Britain, smallpox is still taking its toll in other parts of Europe.

Smallpox is a virus disease. It has been conquered in Britain, and in many other countries, as a direct result of the vaccination technique introduced by an English doctor, Edward Jenner, in 1798. It is on this account that it plays a vital role in the story of man's fight against his invisible enemy—the virus.

Edward Jenner was born on May 17, 1749, son of the Rev. Stephen Jenner, rector of Rockhampton and vicar of Berkeley in Gloucestershire. Jenner was a countryman by upbringing and by inclination. He took up medicine, and after training at Saint George's Hospital, in London, returned to Berkeley to set up as a general practitioner in the rural surroundings he loved.

Like most countrymen, Dr Jenner was observant. He was interested in natural history and became absorbed in the observation of local animals and birds. Jenner studied the cuckoo and watched how the young bird cleared the nest of other young birds and eggs. His account to the Royal Society astounded the Fellows—this was the first time that this instinct of the cuckoo had been described.

Jenner noticed that the young cuckoo had a small depression in its shoulders which was apparently there to help it in getting rid of the other occupants of the nest.

For many years this example of Jenner's careful observation was accepted with considerable doubt, and eventually was regarded as discredited. But within recent years the cine camera has proved Jenner to be correct—a remarkable tribute to his powers of observation.

This habit of careful, accurate study, combined with a zest for experiment, was to bring Jenner perpetual fame in the world of medicine. It led him to his discovery of vaccination, which enables us to protect ourselves from smallpox. And it gave mankind its first great weapon against the virus.

During the eighteenth century, when Jenner was in practice, smallpox had become rife in Britain. The annual deaths in London alone were more than 1000. In 1772 nearly 4000 people died. And London in those days was a small city. For every person that died of smallpox, many others survived but were disfigured for life by the pock marks on the skin.

Though smallpox was most dangerous in the towns where people were crowded together, it was also common in the country districts. Jenner, as a doctor, was familiar enough with the disease.

In the course of his work Jenner—the observant naturalist—noticed an unusual attitude to smallpox on the part of some country people. He heard one young farm worker proclaiming that she could not catch smallpox because she had had another disease called cowpox.

This disease, cowpox, was common among cattle, but it could be passed on to human beings in contact with the animals. It was a mild disease, but familiar to country people. And the belief was fairly well established that people who had suffered from cowpox would not take smallpox. They were in some way immune to the more dangerous disease.

Jenner heard these curious stories, and he began to wonder about them. Were they simply old wives' tales? Or had they some basis in fact? He determined to find out.

Jenner began to keep watch on people who had had cowpox; and eventually he came to the conclusion that their claims were true. They were in fact immune to smallpox as a result of having had the milder disease.

Once he had satisfied himself about this Jenner decided to experiment with cowpox in order to find out whether it could be used deliberately as a protection against smallpox.

In May 1796 Jenner made his first experiment. Taking some of the matter from a pustule on the finger of Sarah Nelmes, a dairymaid suffering from cowpox, he inoculated a young boy with it. The boy, James Phipps, became infected with cowpox. The disease was mild, and the boy quickly recovered.

On July 1 Jenner inoculated the boy with matter from an eruption on the skin of a smallpox patient. But James Phipps remained unharmed. His dose of cowpox which he had suffered two months before had protected him from the deadlier smallpox.

Jenner realized the importance of his discovery to a world in which millions suffered from smallpox every year. In 1797 he presented an account of his work to the President of the Royal Society.

But Jenner's paper was rejected. He was advised that publication would endanger the reputation that his earlier papers had gained for him. So, after adding further information to it, Jenner published it privately in the following year. It was called " An Enquiry into the Cause and Effects of the Variolæ Vaccinæ, a disease discovered in some of the Western Counties of England, particularly Gloucestershire, and known by the name of Cowpox."

The treatise was widely read, and Jenner's discovery stimulated others into action. Soon doctors were sending to him for supplies of the lymph, or fluid, taken from the sores of cowpox patients.

One London doctor was supplied by Jenner with a sample of dried lymph taken from a cowpox lesion in a child. The lymph was sent inside a quill—a method of transport that seems strange in these days of sealed and sterilized glass tubes.

Medicine in those days was still very much a matter of trial and error. Jenner himself could not explain why cowpox lymph should protect a patient against smallpox. And it was inevitable that the lymph should be used for treating other ailments as well. One surgeon, for example, tried cowpox lymph against irritation caused by a hip disease. His patient was not cured of his disease, but by way of recompense he became immune to smallpox.

Gradually, as experiments confirmed the value of Jenner's discovery, the technique of vaccination against smallpox spread throughout the world.

In 1800 Jenner personally vaccinated the entire 85th Regiment. And in 1802 Parliament voted him the sum of £10,000 in recognition of his services and as some compensation for the personal losses suffered as a result of his intensive vaccination research.

By this time vaccination had become common practice in America. Smallpox, after its introduction to the New World by a Negro slave of Cortez in 1520, had caused an epidemic which killed millions of people. Since that time it had remained a serious medical problem in America, and vaccination came as a godsend.

On January 26, 1823, Edward Jenner died at his home in Berkeley, honoured throughout the world for his work on smallpox. By his careful, persistent work he had given us our first real protection against the invisible enemy—the virus.

At the time of Jenner's death doctors were still struggling in the dark against disease. Half a century was to pass before the idea of tiny living micro-organisms, or germs, became established as the cause of infectious disease.

Smallpox, like any other disease, was simply an ailment of the body caused by anything from the influence of the moon to the presence of an injurious vapour in the air.

Jenner, therefore, carried out his vaccination work on a basis of experimental observations. He noticed that cowpox protected from smallpox, and applied his observations in practice. But, in doing so, he knew nothing of the existence of any smallpox virus, or invisible germ, whose multiplication inside the body was causing the disease. He simply realized that one mild disease was able to stimulate the body in some way so that it could protect itself against the other more dangerous disease.

To-day we recognize smallpox as a virus disease. We have identified the infectious agent as a sub-microscopic organism which can live and reproduce itself inside the human body.

We believe that cowpox and smallpox are fundamentally similar diseases, caused by the same type of virus infecting different animals. In the cow this virus produces the mild disease we recognize as cowpox; in man it causes the much more serious disease of smallpox.

Although the cowpox and the smallpox viruses are related one to another, they are not identical. When the cowpox virus is injected into a human being, as it is during vaccination, it causes a disease less dangerous than the original smallpox virus. Yet the diseases are similar in their symptoms and effects.

This ability to modify its 'personality' is a characteristic of the virus. It is particularly evident in the case of the smallpox and cowpox viruses, which appear to be modifications of the same sub-microscopic organism.

The virus that has lived inside the cow has been affected by its environment. It has altered in some way so that it is milder in its reaction to human beings, while remaining fundamentally the same virus. When it is injected into man it brings the natural defences of the body into action, which are able to cope with this particular type of virus and with the dangerous smallpox virus as well.

According to modern ideas, the injection of cowpox viruses into human beings stimulates the release of special 'antibodies' into the bloodstream. These antibodies are specific in their action; they are designed to deal with individual types of invading germ. Antibodies generated for attacking measles viruses, for example, will not be able to protect the body against chickenpox.

But the antibodies released when cowpox virus is injected into the body are able to deal with smallpox virus as well. The two viruses are merely modifications of the same organism. Vaccination with a cowpox type of virus, therefore, such as children are given in Britain, releases a spate of natural defenders into the bloodstream which cope with the invading cowpox viruses. The antibodies then remain in the blood ready to destroy any more dangerous smallpox virus which might make its way into the body.

Nowadays vaccination is carried out with lymph taken from calves or sheep that have been infected with virus 'handed down' for more than a hundred years. When the animals have developed eruptions on the skin they are killed and the lymph is scraped from the skin. This lymph contains supplies of virus. Careful inspection of the animals reduces to a minimum any risk of contamination by dangerous germs. And the lymph itself is treated to ensure its purity before being used for vaccination.

In recent years tests carried out on the virus in this lymph that is used for vaccination have shown that it is not identical with the virus of cowpox occurring naturally to-day. The continued passage of virus from one infected animal to another, and its possible modification by direct passage between human beings practised during the early nineteenth century, have brought about changes in the virus. This 'vaccinia' virus used for vaccination is very much closer to smallpox itself than is the cowpox virus from which it came originally. It still causes a mild disease in man. But it is a different disease from the one that Jenner gave to his 'cowpox' patients a century and a half ago.

Vaccination remains the basis of our methods of protection against virus diseases to-day. We cannot destroy the virus in the bloodstream by means of chemical drugs like penicillin or the sulphonamides. These drugs will kill many disease-producing germs or bacteria, such as we can study under the ordinary microscope. But they are of little direct value against the midget semi-living organism, the virus.

To protect ourselves from viruses we must fall back upon the vaccination technique discovered by Edward Jenner. We give ourselves an injection of some harmless form of virus, and so stimulate the body to defend itself naturally against more dangerous strains of the same invader.

Behind vaccination lies the assumption that an individual virus can exist in modified forms, some less virulent than others. In the case of smallpox we know that this is the case, and Nature has arranged things so that the different viruses are living an independent existence in their own particular environments. Jenner was fortunate in having cowpox ready to hand, providing him with a mild form of smallpox virus that he could use for vaccination.

Smallpox virus is unusual in the facility with which it seems to adapt itself to life in different surroundings. The vaccinia virus now used for supplying lymph is, as we have seen, different from the original cowpox virus; its experiences during the last century or so have altered it in subtle ways. But there is also another form of 'smallpox' virus that exists naturally in man. This virus is a mild form of the dangerous smallpox virus; it causes a human disease called alastrim, which was common in Britain and other western countries in the years before World War II.

Alastrim is not a dangerous disease in the sense that smallpox is. Yet an attack of alastrim will confer immunity to smallpox; the viruses are so similar that the antibodies generated by one will be effective against the other.

The history of smallpox is a story of periodic outbreaks of severe epidemics. Britain was devastated by smallpox during the eighteenth century; it has been estimated that 60 million people died of smallpox throughout the world during that century. Yet for long periods of time smallpox seems to have remained quiescent. The disease would almost disappear from great areas of the world, perhaps for centuries, until in due course an epidemic would again bring death and disfigurement to millions of people.

These waves of smallpox may be a result of the existence of viruses of different virulence. If alastrim became endemic, for example, people who suffered from this mild disease during childhood would be protected from attack by the more dangerous smallpox virus. Alastrim would, in effect, act as a form of widespread vaccination. This would prevent any epidemic of smallpox spreading as it does among unprotected people. Smallpox would die away until, perhaps, the alastrim itself disappeared, leaving people at the mercy of the dangerous smallpox virus.

So far as we know, this ability to exist in several modified 'strains' is a characteristic of viruses, and it is evidence of the living nature of these missing-link organisms. The phenomenon is associated with all living things; it is a result of 'mutation.'

Mutation is a natural process that causes offspring to differ from their parents. It is the breakaway from in- herited characteristics that causes differences between

individuals in a species. In human beings mutation helps
to give us all the infinite variations in human personality.
In animals and plants it enables us to develop different
strains and varieties that serve us in so many different
ways. And in viruses it provides us with strains of varied
virulence, each causing its own version of any particular
virus disease.

Virus mutation, in allowing us to protect ourselves by
vaccination with a mild strain, is of infinite value to us. But
at the same time it holds a constant threat in that it can
give rise to a new strain more dangerous than the original
virus. This, as we shall see later, is a very real danger in
the case of human virus diseases like influenza and poliomyelitis.

In Britain and other countries where public health
organization has reached a high standard of efficiency
smallpox has been completely stamped out. Vaccination
has undoubtedly been the most important single factor in
our elimination of the disease.

With smallpox no longer a serious threat opinion has
tended to harden against compulsory vaccination. No
matter how carefully vaccination is carried out there is
always some danger of unpleasant consequences in isolated
cases. And it is natural that people will avoid taking any
risks with their children's health that are not regarded as
absolutely necessary. At any sign of an epidemic starting,
for example from an infected person entering the country,
emergency vaccination can be carried out immediately on
any ' contacts,' and the danger of a major epidemic is comparatively slight.

The development of air-travel has increased the danger
of introducing smallpox into a country like Britain. When
people travelled by sea from Eastern countries smallpox
would have plenty of time to make its appearance before
the ship reached northern European ports. The incubation
time of the disease is short—only about a week. But now
that we can travel from the East to Britain in a matter of

a day or two there is a considerable risk of a smallpox carrier spending several days in the country before the disease is diagnosed. In that time the number of contacts could be so great that emergency vaccination might be inadequate to stop an epidemic.

3

The Second Success - Yellow Fever

THE course of history has been changed as much by disease as by the force of arms. Epidemics have swept across vast continents and subjugated empires. Germs have won battles and crippled powerful armies.

In this unending struggle between the microbe and mankind our invisible virus has played a major role. Small-pox, as we have seen, spread death and suffering over the civilized world for centuries. To-day, as a result of Jenner's work on vaccination, we have its measure. But there are other virus diseases which have been more difficult to control. One of these is the disease called Yellow Fever.

Yellow fever is a disease of the hot, damp countries of the tropics. During the eighteenth and nineteenth centuries, when the western world was building up its colonies and empires, yellow fever established a reign of terror over European settlers in almost every hot country of the world. In North and South America, in the West Indies and in Africa, people died in their thousands from the dread disease with its retching and its foul black vomit. Wherever Europeans settled in the tropical countries they were attacked by yellow fever. The West Coast of Africa became "The White Man's Grave" largely through the prevalence of yellow fever. Yet the native populations in such places seemed to be protected by some form of natural immunity.

Obviously protection was possible against attack by yellow fever. Nature did it for the natives. But immigrants from countries where yellow fever was not endemic were apparently helpless against the disease.

The Haitian Republic was established with the help of yellow fever. In 1801 Napoleon sent 25,000 men to Haiti to quell a Negro revolt. The French won their battle with the native troops. But they could do nothing against attack by yellow fever. In 1803 the remnants of Napoleon's expeditionary force set sail for home. Only 3000 men were left of the original army; 22,000 had died of yellow fever.

Throughout the nineteenth century the Southern States of America suffered heavily from yellow fever epidemics. Six years after the adoption of the Constitution an epidemic in Philadelphia killed more than a tenth of the city's population. The disease struck terror in the city. Doctors could do nothing to fight it. They had no understanding of its cause and were willing to try any remedy that was recommended for its control.

The College of Physicians in Philadelphia issued a manifesto of suggestions to the people. Burning gunpowder, they said, would help to keep down the spread of the disease. Cannon were fired off at street corners in the city. But they did nothing to keep the yellow fever in check.

In 1878 a wave of fever struck New Orleans and swept through the town and up the valley of the Mississippi. It killed 20,000 people. In Memphis half the population fled the city. Yet in a short time 6000 died. Nothing could be done to save them.

To-day we know that yellow fever is a virus disease. Though smallpox, during the nineteenth century, was being steadily overcome as Jenner's vaccination was adopted, there was no such protection against yellow fever. No convenient animal disease existed to provide protection in the way that cowpox did against smallpox.

Throughout the century scientists struggled to solve the problem of yellow fever. They searched for methods of protection against the disease. And they tried to find out how it spread from man to man.

As the germ theory became established doctors began searching the blood of yellow fever victims to try and identify the microbe that was causing the disease. But yellow fever, like smallpox, had no recognizable germ associated with it. The germ was there. But it was a virus, invisible through the microscope and able to pass through the finest filter.

Much of the mystery of yellow fever came from the illogical way it struck down its victims during an epidemic. Smallpox obviously spread by direct contact with infected persons. But yellow fever would break out spontaneously in many parts of a town. And there would be no noticeable pattern of infection. How then did the disease spread?

In 1881 a Cuban doctor, Carlos Juan Finlay, suggested that the disease was carried by a tiny striped mosquito which infected its victims as it bit them. Finlay went so far as to show that mosquitoes feeding on a yellow fever patient could pass on the infection when they subsequently bit a human volunteer.

But for some strange reason this direct proof of the fact that mosquitoes carry the disease was largely disregarded. It was treated as an interesting academic experiment. But its full implications, which could have brought action that might have saved thousands of lives, were ignored for nearly twenty years.

To-day we know that Finlay's theory was correct. It explained the strange nature of the yellow fever epidemics, when people caught the disease for no apparent reason. They were being infected by mosquitoes which could carry the disease swiftly from one end of a city to the other.

The Spanish-American War was the stimulus that finally carried through the conclusive yellow fever research. American troops fell in their thousands to yellow fever, which caused more casualties than the war itself.

By this time the part played by mosquitoes in the spread of other tropical diseases was becoming well established.

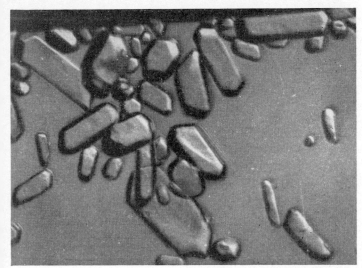

Photo Dr F. L. Schaffer and C. E. Schwerdt

POLIOMYELITIS

(*Above*) Crystals of this virus each containing millions of virus particles
arranged with geometrical precision alongside one another.

(*Right*) These fluffy-
looking balls are par-
ticles of Type 1 polio-
myelitis virus photo-
graphed through the
electron microscope.

Photo The National Foundation for Infantile Paralysis, New York

COMMON COLD RESEARCH

These quarters, at the research unit near Salisbury, are used to house the
human 'guinea pigs.'

THE COMMON COLD VIRUS

An electron micrograph showing a strain of the virus magnified more than
70,000 times

Patrick Manson had shown that elephantiasis was caused by a tiny worm carried from man to man by the mosquito. This same insect had been identified as the carrier of the malaria parasite. It was natural, particularly after Finlay's experiments in 1881, that the mosquito should be high on the list of suspects as the transmitter of yellow fever.

Under the leadership of Major Walter Reed, the United States' Yellow Fever Commission began its work in Cuba in 1900. Once again they searched for yellow fever germs in the blood of patients. And once again they failed to find any.

To test the mosquito theory three men volunteered to be bitten by mosquitoes which had fed on yellow fever victims. They all developed fever. Two recovered, but the third, Dr Jesse Lazear—a member of the Commission—died on September 25, 1900. He was the first of many who were to give their lives in the study of this terrible disease.

Although the experiment showed again that the mosquito could transmit yellow fever, it did not prove that the disease could not be spread in other ways as well. Another experiment was therefore carried out to find out whether yellow fever could be transmitted by direct infection.

Two small cottages were built and every precaution was taken to make sure that mosquitoes could not get in or out. In the first cottage volunteers slept in beds and blankets that had been soiled by yellow fever patients. They even wore pyjamas which had been used by patients who had died. Yet not one of the volunteers was infected.

In the second cottage another volunteer, John Moran, spent the night in clean, new sheets with plenty of air flowing through the close-mesh mosquito netting on the windows. But to keep him company he had fifteen female mosquitoes which had been allowed to feed on yellow fever patients.

Moran was bitten as he slept; he developed yellow fever from which he eventually recovered.

So, by 1901, it had been proved beyond all doubt that

mosquitoes were indeed responsible for spreading yellow
fever germs. Reed and his team showed that a house-
haunting mosquito, *Aëdes ægypti*, was the carrier of yellow
fever in Cuba. They continued their experiments until
eventually the pattern of infection was established.

From two to six days after being bitten by the mosquito
the victims develop fever. In the mosquito there is a similar
incubation period after it has fed on an infected human
being. For about twelve days the mosquito will not pass
on its infection to a person on which it feeds. The virus,
during this time, is believed to be making its way from
the insect's stomach to the salivary glands. After the virus
has reached these glands the mosquito can inject a dose of
virus into any victim on which it feeds. For the rest of its
life, which may be several months, the mosquito remains
infective.

This double hiatus in the yellow fever cycle explained
the strange fortnightly waves of fever that occurred in a
typical epidemic. The time is governed by the two
development periods needed by the yellow fever virus—
one in man, and one in the mosquito.

When Reed and his colleagues were carrying out their
yellow fever work the idea of an invisible germ—a virus
—had become accepted. Iwanowski's experiments with
tobacco mosaic virus had proved that infection could be
passed from plant to plant by contamination with the clear,
filtered sap of an infected plant. There were no visible
germs in the sap, but there was some infectious agent in it.

Reed, unable to find any visible yellow fever germ in the
blood of victims of the disease, suspected that yellow fever
must be caused by a virus. John Carroll, a member of the
Yellow Fever Commission, injected the filtered blood of
infected soldiers into three volunteers. The blood was entirely free of visible germs. But the volunteers went down
with yellow fever.

Until the electron microscope was developed during
World War II the existence of the yellow fever virus had

to be taken on trust. But our inability to see the virus did
not prevent a great deal of research being carried out during the first half of this century. Methods were devised for
detecting the virus and estimating its concentration. Its
behaviour inside the mosquito was followed in detail.

During the ten to twelve days of incubation inside the
insect the dose of virus acquired by the mosquito as it fed
on its infected human victim increases inside the insect.
The virus multiplies, and within a month there is ten times
as much inside the mosquito as there was originally. For
the rest of its life the insect acts as a dangerous, mobile
hypodermic needle, injecting a supply of virus into any
human being on which it feeds.

The recognition of yellow fever as a virus disease
brought it into line with smallpox. But there was no way
of organizing large-scale protection against yellow fever by
vaccination. There was no convenient animal disease
which could be used to develop a mild form of the fever
in man.

But there was another way in which yellow fever could
be attacked. Unlike smallpox, which was carried from one
person to another by direct infection through the breath,
yellow fever could only be transmitted by a mosquito. So,
by destroying the mosquitoes, the spread of yellow fever
could be halted.

This has remained the basis of yellow fever control in
great areas of the world up to the present time. It was
believed at first that yellow fever was doomed to disappear
from the earth. Like the dodo, the virus would be exter-
minated completely; all that we had to do was to wipe out
the *Aëdes ægypti* mosquitoes wherever they were to be
found. Once all infected insects could be destroyed the
yellow fever virus would inevitably disappear.

With this as the ultimate goal, man set to work to get
rid of *Aëdes ægypti* from the tropical danger-areas where
it was doing most harm.

In Cuba an anti-mosquito campaign was immediately

successful. Yellow fever was eradicated completely from the island by 1910.

On the Isthmus of Panama another great campaign was fought against the yellow fever mosquito. The building of the Panama Canal, which had been abandoned by the French owing to yellow fever epidemics, was finally completed. During early attempts more than a third of the white workers had died of yellow fever. By wiping out the fever-carrying mosquitoes Surgeon-General W. G. Gorgas was able to carry through the building of the Canal.

Gradually yellow fever was overcome wherever the mosquito could be brought under control. From towns and cities and crowded localities the spectre of this age-old disease was raised as its insect host was ruthlessly destroyed.

By 1925 Central America and the West Indies had been cleared of the disease, and all that remained to free the entire western hemisphere was to destroy a patch of fever country in Brazil.

But the yellow fever threat was being underestimated. In 1932 Brazil suffered an epidemic of yellow fever in a district where the *Aëdes ægypti* mosquito was not to be found. Soon research showed that other types of mosquito carried the yellow fever virus too. Among them were insects living normally in the jungle, away from human settlements!

Aëdes ægypti is a mosquito that inhabits human settlements; it is comparatively easy to eradicate it from a town or village. But jungle mosquitoes enjoy life out of touch with man; they feed on the blood of wild animals instead.

The discovery that these jungle mosquitoes carried yellow fever virus indicated that some wild animals must be infected with the virus too. Research carried out by scientists of the Rockefeller Foundation quickly showed that this was in fact the case.

Expeditions penetrated into tropical jungles; more than 2000 animals were captured and examined. Many of them, including monkeys and rodents, opossums, anteaters, sloths, and armadillos, were found to have yellow fever virus in their blood.

This discovery of a vast pool of infection in the insects and animals of the tropical jungle dispelled once and for all any prospect of eradicating yellow fever entirely from the earth. Towns and villages could be cleared of the disease by mosquito control. But in the jungle and in the lightly-populated countrysides mosquitoes could not be wiped out. In such places yellow fever must remain a constant threat. Only by finding a protection against the disease itself could the menace of the virus be overcome.

Yellow fever, like most virus diseases, is a difficult subject for research. The only laboratory animal available for experiments until 1928 was man himself; more valuable lives have been lost in yellow fever research than in the investigation of any other infectious disease.

In 1928 a Yellow Fever Commission of the Rockefeller Foundation working at Lagos in West Africa discovered that Indian monkeys were susceptible to infection by yellow fever. Within a year Adrian Stokes, a British member of the team, had died of yellow fever. But the discovery that he and his colleagues made was to open the way to our modern methods of protection against the disease.

Two years later a London-trained South African scientist, Dr Max Theiler, found that yellow fever virus injected into the brain of a mouse would multiply and cause disease. Man was no longer alone in suffering from the attack of yellow fever virus.

This was a discovery of vital importance. It meant that there was now the possibility of cultivating a modified virus in an animal, just as the smallpox virus produced cowpox virus when grown in a cow. If a modified yellow fever virus could be cultivated in such a way that it caused a milder disease in a man than yellow fever itself then it would be possible to use it for vaccination against its virulent relative.

Repeated experiments were carried out, in which yellow
fever virus was grown in mouse brains. Gradually the virus
modified itself as it grew in unaccustomed surroundings.
And eventually a strain was produced which caused only
a mild form of yellow fever when injected into monkeys.

This was progress indeed. But still the stage had not
been reached at which the virus was suitable for human
vaccination. This final step was taken when the virus was
cultivated in new surroundings—living chick embryos
suspended in serum.

Growing in the living cells of the chick embryo, the
virus again changed to a new strain under the influence of
its unusual environment. It became modified into a virus
that caused only a mild disease in man. And yet it brought
the body's defences into action so that they were ready to
tackle the normal yellow fever virus that found its way
into the bloodstream from a mosquito bite.

This new strain of yellow fever virus was called 17D.
It has done for yellow fever what cowpox vaccine did for
smallpox.

Like all viruses, the 17D yellow fever virus will multiply
only inside an appropriate living cell. Supplies of virus to
be used for vaccination must be grown in the living tissue
of chick embryos. This is not an easy manufacturing technique for mass-production purposes. But the demand for
17D virus was so great that plans were made immediately
for cultivating virus on an enormous scale.

Injected into man, 17D virus causes a mild disease just
as cowpox virus does in the case of smallpox vaccination.
The natural defences of the body are stimulated and antibodies are set free into the bloodstream. Once again the
antibodies are designed to deal with the particular virus
that has entered the blood. And having destroyed the 17D,
they are ready and waiting to attack any subsequent infection by a virus of this sort.

But 17D is essentially a mild strain of yellow fever virus,
and the antibodies can cope as effectively with the danger-

ous virus injected by a mosquito as it seeks its feed of blood.

The antibodies generated in this way by 17D vaccination will remain effective for as long as six years. People in yellow fever districts are therefore vaccinated with 17D every five years.

So, in the years between the two World Wars, science developed yet another weapon in the unending struggle against disease. Yellow fever, which had cast its shadow over the tropical countries for hundreds of years, was on the retreat. A second virus disease was being countered by the application of its own characteristic property of mutation, or spontaneous change.

Even so, the development of a means of protection is only the first step in fighting a major disease. Mass inoculation or vaccination of millions of people is a herculean task. Cultivation of the harmless virus strain for use as vaccine can never be a straightforward job so long as it involves the use of living matter in which the virus can multiply.

Vast outbreaks of yellow fever will still occur to-day among susceptible people who have not been adequately protected. Nigeria suffered a terrible epidemic during 1946.

But great progress is steadily being made in face of the tremendous difficulties. Over fifteen million people, for example, have been vaccinated against yellow fever in French West Africa alone.

Inevitably there are dangers to be faced when living viruses are injected deliberately into human beings. The fact that 17D vaccine contains a living virus means that it is possible for other viruses to contaminate it without being destroyed during subsequent treatment.

During World War II every United States soldier destined for the tropics was vaccinated with 17D. By April 1942 80,000 of these servicemen were suffering from a type of jaundice called hepatitis. The infection was traced to certain batches of 17D yellow fever vaccine which had been made with the help of human blood serum containing hepatitis virus.

To-day we know something about the yellow fever virus itself. It has now been photographed through the electron microscope.

This midget virus lives out its cycle of life between the mosquito and the monkey. It is primarily a disease of animals rather than of man. Under natural surroundings, in the jungle for example, yellow fever circulates between the monkey and the mosquito, maintaining the necessary pool of infection in each. Under such conditions Nature seems to operate her familiar rule of "live and let live." The monkeys often develop a natural resistance to the yellow fever virus. They suffer from the disease, but are not destroyed by it. The virus thus maintains a situation where it can itself survive.

In many parts of Africa, where yellow fever has over the centuries become a part of normal life, the native population has similarly arrived at a compromise agreement with the yellow fever virus.

Mothers pass the protective agents to their children, and the children are able to withstand attack by yellow fever. Their natural defences are ready, just as though they had been vaccinated.

But the newcomer to a yellow fever district has no such natural protection. His safeguard against the virus must lie in vaccination with the modified strain that can bring his natural defences into play.

In 1951 Dr Max Theiler of the Rockefeller Institute was awarded the Nobel Prize for Medicine in recognition of his work in developing yellow fever vaccine. With the award we remember the victims, six from the Institute itself, who have died while carrying out yellow fever research.

4

Influenza

IN the early summer of 1918, as the First World War was straining towards its climax, the Allied armies were attacked from within by an enemy more dangerous than the Central Powers. Influenza joined the struggle; and during the following year it was to bring more deaths and suffering than the great World War itself had caused.

In three vicious waves influenza swept round the world in 1918 and 1919. More than 7,000,000 deaths from the disease were recorded during the terrible pandemic, and it is certain that the actual figure was nearer 15,000,000. Altogether 500 million people had influenza in this worst flare-up of disease that the world has ever known. And against the attack of the tiny virus—for influenza is the work of a virus—we were virtually powerless. We had no drugs to fight the germ and we had no vaccination technique to protect ourselves by rousing our natural defences.

Since 1918 scientists and doctors have worked desperately to find an effective way of fighting influenza. The memory of the post-war epidemic has been a stimulus to research, and the world has been haunted by the fear of a repetition of the disaster.

So far we have escaped. Influenza has stayed with us, but no world-wide outbreak has occurred to compare with that of 1918.

Since then influenza has kept up a steady attack on the well-being of the world. Its savage outburst has been followed by a period of quiescence, during which the virus has been keeping us from our work and sapping our mental and physical strength.

Every year influenza and the common cold between them cost us 1000 million man hours of work in Britain alone. An epidemic can treble the figure. Influenza is responsible for more disruption of work in Britain than all our other diseases combined.

It is not surprising, therefore, that in our twentieth-century battle with the virus we have concentrated our attack upon the virus of influenza. Here we have a germ that holds our western world in bondage as complete as that imposed by malaria in tropical countries. We have, as yet, no really satisfactory protection against it. But medical research is now organized against influenza, and our understanding of the disease has increased excitingly during recent years. From this understanding of influenza has come most of our modern knowledge of the nature of animal viruses.

Influenza has been with us for at least a thousand years. Medical records suggest that there was a serious outbreak in 1173, and there are indications of epidemics coming in cycles of every twenty or forty years.

A world-wide wave of disease spread to Europe from China in 1782. It was almost certainly influenza as we know it to-day. But at that time the name influenza was given to any epidemic which was regarded as the result of evil ' influences ' inflicted on mankind by an unkind fate.

In Britain the registration of deaths was introduced in 1837, and diseases and ailments gradually took on more precise distinctions one from another. The name influenza became identified with the respiratory, catarrhal disease so familiar to us to-day.

An examination of the death rates in Britain since 1837 shows three great 'flu epidemics separated by periods of thirty to forty years during which the disease at times almost disappeared.

The epidemic of 1847–48 was followed by a respite from

influenza during which the death rate dropped to only two per million in 1889. Then in 1890 influenza struck with characteristic violence, and deaths from 'flu rose to 574 per million in England and Wales.

For almost thirty years 'flu remained at an epidemic level, with the death rate varying between 120 and 293 per million. Then in 1918 came the worst epidemic of all. The death rate reached its record peak of 3129 per million, and, as we have seen, millions of people were struck down in almost every country of the world.

Since this last pandemic of influenza the death rate has dropped again (29 per million in 1948) and the disease has been content to smoulder steadily without bursting into flame.

The seriousness of the 1918 epidemic was sufficient to shock the world into urgent effort. 'Flu became a high priority job for medicine, and it has remained so ever since.

The epidemic came in three distinct waves. It began in May 1918, and was almost certainly brought to Europe by the American troops. The virus found ideal conditions among the soldiers herded together along the Western front. All the Allies suffered simultaneously, and at first it was thought that biological warfare had been started by the Germans.

But by July 'flu had attacked the Central Powers with undiminished force. During the early summer the virus spread a wave of disease over the whole of Europe.

This first wave soon spent itself. The disease was, in general, mild. And the fatal casualties were few, although the latter cases suggested an increasing virulence in the virus.

During the late autumn and winter of 1918 the influenza virus struck again. With incredible speed it swept round the world, through Europe, Asia, Africa, and America.

This second wave of 'flu brought with it a disease more dangerous than the first. There were often complications in the lungs and breathing passages, and the death rate was high. It was almost as though the virus had become more vicious in its temperament since its attacks of a month or two earlier.

In March 1919 the third wave of the great pandemic began. By the time it had spent itself the world was reeling under one of the worst blows it had ever experienced. In a few months the invisible virus of influenza had brought more death and suffering than the armies of the Powers had caused during their four years of war.

Deaths caused by influenza are usually among older people, particularly those already weakened by other ailments and diseases. Influenza will shorten the lives of people suffering from tuberculosis, for example, bringing death a few years earlier than it would normally take place.

The 1918 influenza virus was unusual in that it killed young people rather than the older ones. This tendency remained even after the worst of the epidemic was over. There was a flare-up of influenza in 1920, but it was not so widespread as in the previous two years. Again, the virus concentrated its activities against young people.

Gradually the pattern of infection changed; and by 1929 the virus had reverted to its normal behaviour. Once again it was causing death among the aged and infirm, rather than among the young.

The 1918 pandemic had one invaluable result. It brought home to the world how dangerous this disease of influenza could be. Immediately teams of scientists and doctors set to work to study influenza. This research continues to-day and has become one of the vital sectors in our attack on the general problem of disease. Influenza research is tackling the most efficient enemy of all—the virus.

By 1919 it had become certain that influenza was in fact a virus disease. Filtered sputum from influenza patients was injected into the throats and noses of twenty-four healthy volunteers. Six of these had recovered quite recently from 'flu. Within a day or two the eighteen volunteers who had not previously had 'flu went down with the disease. The other six remained unaffected.

These and other experiments showed that the disease was caused by some germ in the filtered sputum. A germ so small that it passed a bacterium filter and could not be seen through the microscope. That is to say, a virus.

In 1933 Sir Patrick Laidlaw clinched the matter when he isolated the human influenza virus at the National Institute for Medical Research at Hampstead.

As in the case of smallpox and yellow fever, people who had recently recovered from the disease were usually immune. This immunity, in the case of influenza, does not appear to last for very long. But it may account for the interval of twenty to thirty years between pandemics. The virus cannot run amok until the proportion of protected people in the general population shrinks to a certain critical size.

Protection against attack by influenza has followed the pattern traced by smallpox and yellow fever. A person who has had influenza is, for a time, protected automatically against further attack by the same disease. The natural defences of the body have been stimulated and are ready to tackle fresh invaders.

Since 1918 scientists have been trying to find ways of inducing this stimulation artificially. It can be done, as it is in the case of smallpox and yellow fever, by injecting a mild strain of the virus into the body. But there is another technique which can be used when a suitable mild strain is not available. The virus can be 'killed,' or inactivated, by treating it with chemicals such as formalin. This virus can no longer multiply inside the body to cause disease; but the virus 'corpses' will stimulate the body-defences into action just as living virus does. Antibodies are generated, even though the invading germs are already dead.

No matter which technique of vaccination is used, we come up against the usual difficulties inherent in cultiva-

ting the supplies of virus that are needed. The nature of the
germ is such that it cannot multiply outside the appropriate cell. Some living medium had to be found in which
the influenza virus could be grown conveniently and
cheaply. Human beings are inconvenient and expensive as
laboratory animals.

In 1940 Professor F. M. Burnet, an Australian, developed
a method of cultivating the influenza virus inside hens'
eggs. This gave us a practicable means of growing the
virus on a large scale and thereby making a vaccine.

By 1941 a vaccine for influenza had been made and we
had taken a step towards self-protection against the virus.

Burnet's discovery was made originally with virus that
had been grown in the nasal passage of ferrets. Ferrets
are among the few animals that are susceptible to human
influenza.

At first the virus grew in the egg membranes without
harming the embryo itself. But after many transfers from
egg to egg the virus began to change and attack its new
host. Finally it became so virulent against the chick
embryo that it killed it within two or three days.

Here, once again, was an example of a virus undergoing
some sort of mutation. Growing in a new environment, a
modified strain of virus was produced which flourished in
the egg.

This discovery of the living egg as a host for influenza
opened the way towards the production of vaccine in sufficient quantity for practical use. During the Second World
War this production of influenza vaccine was in fact
accomplished, and experiments began immediately to find
out whether it could protect us successfully from the
disease.

Unfortunately protection against influenza is anything
but a straightforward problem. There are difficulties which
have prevented us making entirely satisfactory use of vaccines, and the problem is still with us.

Two main types of influenza virus are now recognized—

Type A and Type B. Each causes the disease we describe as influenza in human beings. But a vaccine made from one type of influenza virus does not protect us against the other.

Moreover the influenza virus appears to be an unusually fickle one. It changes its character by mutation easily and quickly; new strains of virus are formed which may be almost identical in their effects but do not react in the same way to antibodies in the blood.

Many different strains of Type A virus have been identified since the virus was discovered in 1933. Antibodies generated by one strain are not necessarily effective against another.

Type B virus was not isolated until 1940. It caused the California epidemic of 1936.

The pattern of influenza epidemics can now be followed with some precision, and it seems that Type A epidemics follow each other at intervals of two or three years. Type B epidemics are usually less frequent and are separated by as much as six years.

The onset of an epidemic is controlled by many factors. The weather conditions play an important part, and influenza prefers to spread in winter or in spring. It will only cause an epidemic if there are sufficient unprotected people to allow the infection to spread.

The antibodies generated by an attack of 'flu will probably remain effective for five years or more. If the influenza virus was less susceptible to mutation we could rely on being immune at least for several years. But the virus changes so easily from one strain to another that it can side-step the natural defences that were stimulated by its earlier attacks.

Protection against the influenza virus therefore requires a rapid and efficient organization for identifying the type of virus that is causing an epidemic. This is the job of the World Influenza Centre set up at Mill Hill, in London, in 1948. Here, under the leadership of Dr Christopher

Andrewes, scientists are studying influenza as a world problem.

Into the World Influenza Centre come samples of sputum from influenza patients all over the world. Nobody can forecast which type of influenza is going to strike next, but by identifying samples quickly we can keep track of the viruses before the epidemic gets out of hand.

Once the type of 'flu is known vaccines can be made and used to provide protection against the germ.

The World Influenza Centre proved how invaluable it could be almost as soon as it had been created. In the winter of 1948 an epidemic of influenza swept over Europe, starting from Sardinia. Travelling rapidly through Italy, France, Switzerland, and Austria, the virus reached Britain within a few weeks. Soon it was causing 300 deaths a week in Britain.

Meanwhile samples of sputum had been sent—packed in dry ice at $-76°C$.—from southern Europe to the World Influenza Centre in London. The virus was identified as Type A, and information about it was sent all over the world. Public health authorities were able to prepare to meet the threat of a world-wide epidemic such as we had in 1918.

In the winter of 1950–51 a Type A epidemic started in Sweden and spread to Britain via Newcastle. But by the time the virus had crossed the North Sea a sample from Sweden had been identified and we were ready for it.

Making the vaccine can now be done quickly and on a large scale by using eggs. After the eggs have been incubated for ten days they are inoculated with the virus. The tiny holes left in the shell are plugged with paraffin and the eggs incubated again.

For two or three days the virus multiplies inside the living cells of the egg embryo. Then the top of the shell is cut off carefully, the membranes surrounding the embryo are punctured, and blood from the embryo is allowed to mix with the fluid surrounding it. This fluid contains the concentrated influenza virus. As soon as the blood is mixed into it the virus is absorbed from the fluid by the red cells of the blood.

The mixed fluids are then siphoned carefully from the eggs and the red blood cells are separated from the liquid. These cells contain the virus, which can be washed out again from them.

In this way we finish up with a concentrated solution of influenza virus from which the vaccine can be made. If the virus is a virulent one it must be 'killed' before it is used. This can be done by treating it with a suitable antiseptic which destroys its infective power.

Injected into a healthy person, this 'dead' virus is harmless and cannot cause influenza. But the body reacts to the virus just as if it were alive and immediately takes steps to protect itself against attack.

So, as in the case of smallpox and yellow fever, the bloodstream is ready to tackle any live invader of a similar strain.

Much of our information on animal viruses has come from the study of influenza. And one reason for the rapid advance of influenza research has undoubtedly been the discovery of the egg cultivation technique.

But in addition to this scientists have found it possible to measure and assess the growth of influenza virus much more easily than that of any other animal virus.

In carrying out useful experiments of any sort it is always necessary to measure the results. Virus research has presented us with the greatest difficulties in this respect. The 'apparatus' in virus work must inevitably be a living thing. For it is only inside a suitable living cell that the virus can multiply.

Estimating the amount of chemical in a test-tube is usually a simple enough job. But to do the same when the chemical is inside a chicken embryo or a monkey's brain is often an impossible task.

In the early days of influenza research it was found that

the virus, in addition to growing in hens' eggs, would multiply in the lungs of mice. And the effect of the virus on the mouse lung was used as a measure of the quantity of virus. The more virus in a dose, the more consolidation it produced in the mouse's lung. This method of assessing virus was cumbersome and inconvenient. Also it gave only an approximate measurement.

In 1941 there happened one of those accidental discoveries which so often help us out in scientific research. George K. Hirst, working at the Rockefeller Institute for Medical Research in America, was experimenting with the newly-discovered egg-cultivation of influenza virus. He was examining the fluid in the cavities surrounding the chick embryo. This fluid was rich in influenza virus, and during the experiment some of the fluid spilled over into a dish where it mixed with a little blood.

Hirst noticed, to his surprise, that the red blood cells clumped together in the blood as a result of being mixed with influenza virus. He followed up his discovery, and from it devised a test for influenza virus. Moreover, he found that he could use his blood-clumping test as a way of distinguishing between different types of influenza virus.

In spite of our modern knowledge, influenza remains almost as difficult a practical problem as ever. We have epidemics every year, with their steady drain on health and efficiency. And the use of vaccines for protection has not yet been adopted as a standard measure.

Like most other diseases influenza confers immunity on its victims once they have recovered from the attack. But the immunity in the case of influenza is so much more transient than in other diseases. People who had been attacked by the first wave of 'flu during the 1918 pandemic, for example, were attacked again during the second wave which came only a few months later.

It has been suggested that the virus changed even more rapidly than usual through the influence of mustard gas used on the Western Front. We now know that this type of chemical will increase the mutation rate of living things. It may have encouraged the development of virulent strains of virus which caused such havoc in 1918.

If antibodies are to be effective the attacking germ must make its way into the body via the bloodstream. This is where the antibodies can concentrate for attack. But the influenza virus attacks us through our respiratory system. The virus spreads from cell to cell over the surface of the air passages. The antibodies in the blood are denied an opportunity of attacking the virus in force.

In spite of this the use of influenza vaccine has been making progress. If the correct strain of virus is used in making the vaccine, and the dose is given shortly before infection occurs, up to 90 per cent. protection can be expected.

During an epidemic of Type A influenza tests carried out by the United States Army showed that vaccination cut down the influenza rate from 7.11 per cent. to 2.22 per cent. That is to say, the ratio of infection between vaccinated and unprotected was approximately 1 to 3.

In 1945 seven million men of the United States Army were inoculated with mixed Type A and Type B vaccines to provide all-round protection during the 'flu months. The influenza rate declined appreciably as a result.

There is no doubt, therefore, that large-scale vaccination at the proper time and with the appropriate vaccine can do a lot to counter attacks by 'flu. We can fight back against the threat of another " 1918 pandemic " of influenza. Not only have we the prospect of mass inoculation in an emergency, but we have the additional safeguard of our modern drugs. Penicillin, streptomycin, aureomycin, sulpha drugs, and the rest have little or no effect against the virus itself. But they can protect us against many of the bacteria that caused fatal complications in 1918 and 1919.

5

Poliomyelitis - the Modern Plague

In its attack on man the virus has made things difficult for us by insisting on its privilege of multiplying only inside the living cell. We cannot easily divorce the virus from its host and cultivate it at will in our laboratory apparatus. We can study it as a living thing only inside another living thing.

This characteristic has presented unusual difficulties to the scientist wanting to carry out experimental work upon the virus. In some cases reasonably convenient laboratory 'hosts' have been found—for example, the living hen's egg in the study of influenza. But with many viruses we have been less fortunate, and our investigation of the diseases they cause has been held up on that account. Such a virus is the one that is responsible for infantile paralysis, or poliomyelitis.

Polio—as it is commonly known to-day—has become one of the most feared diseases of modern times. Polio concentrates its attack on children, and exhibits no logical pattern of infection. One child in a family will often be struck down, while brothers and sisters will suffer no apparent harm. The disease is often crippling and some-times fatal; its effects can remain for life, with no prospect of complete recovery. Small wonder, then, that polio has become the modern plague.

We know now that poliomyelitis is a virus disease. Once again it is this invisible germ, this living chemical, that can find its way into our bodies and multiply to cause

disease. As a chemical, the polio virus remains a mystery.
Until 1953 we had not seen it even with the help of the
electron microscope. In the winter of that year the polio
virus was photographed for the first time; it is one of the
smallest viruses, less than a hundredth the diameter of an
average bacterium. In 1955 the polio virus was purified
and obtained as crystals—the first animal virus to be isolated in this form.

In spite of its diminutive size, the polio virus is tough.
It is not easily destroyed either by heating or with the help
of chemicals. This tenaciousness is useful to us in our study
of poliomyelitis; it enables us to isolate the virus without
destroying it in the process.

Although we know comparatively little about the polio
virus itself, we have made tremendous progress since
World War II in the study of the disease it causes; we
know much about the behaviour of the virus as an infecting organism.

Polio is often regarded as a disease of modern times. It
has not a history going back for thousands of years, like
smallpox or yellow fever. The first epidemic was reported
in Sweden in 1887, when a new infectious disease swept
through the country causing paralysis in children. In 1894
the United States had its first epidemic in Vermont; 119
people were affected by paralysis.

This terrifying disease was something new; its epidemics
left disablement and death in their train. But as doctors
built up an understanding of the 'new' disease they
realized that it was identical with the disease they already
knew as infantile paralysis.

Infantile paralysis was recognized as a rare but widespread disease in Britain as long ago as 1784. Every year
a few infants would be affected by paralysis during the
first year or two of life. Fortunately the disease was not a
common one; but it was always cropping up.

The outbreaks of poliomyelitis—" inflammation of the
grey marrow of the spinal cord "—were epidemics of the

infantile paralysis that had been known for as long as
medical records existed. But instead of attacking infants
in their early years, the new polio was shifting its attention
to children of school age. Children between five and ten
years old were being attacked, and in increasing numbers.

Since the end of the nineteenth century, when polio
epidemics were first recognized, the disease has spread
throughout the world in its newer and more serious form.
In the United States and in Western Europe, in Canada
and Australia, polio epidemics are anticipated every summer, and they never fail to arrive. Some years they are
worse than others. But polio is always with us.

By 1909 it had been established that polio was a virus
disease. The virus was isolated from the spinal cord of a
child dead from polio; inoculated into the brain of a monkey this virus caused a disease similar to polio in man.
And by repeated inoculation it could be passed on from
one monkey to another.

Most bewildering of all the characteristics of polio is its
reaction to changes in the standard of living. As man
improves the conditions under which he lives he protects
himself increasingly from most infectious diseases. But
polio becomes more widespread and more dangerous as
our living-standards rise. Before the nineteenth century,
when sanitation was primitive and life was squalid by
modern standards, polio as we know it to-day did not exist.
Only as we improved our standards of hygiene and public
health has it found conditions under which it can cause
epidemics. The cleaner and more civilized we become, the
greater is the danger from polio.

In the United States, where living standards are higher
than in most other parts of the world, polio has been increasing its threat from year to year. As a result, research
has been stimulated, and much of the work that has given
us our present understanding of the disease has been carried out in the United States.

Polio is no easy subject for study. It is a highly infectious and dangerous disease. Until quite recently the virus could be grown only in the nervous system of human beings, monkeys, or chimpanzees. This put immense practical difficulties in the way of progress.

In 1949 Dr John F. Enders and his colleagues Dr Robbins and Dr Weller at the Boston Children's Hospital discovered that polio virus could be grown in cultures of non-nervous tissue. This was an immense step forward; it made possible the cultivation of virus on a large scale in the laboratory. Living tissue taken from a monkey can be kept alive in fluid that supplies the living cells with the substances they need. 'Tissue-culture' techniques of this sort are now common practice, and cells will continue to multiply under these conditions for almost any length of time.

When polio virus is added to an appropriate tissue culture of this sort the virus invades the living cells and multiplies as though it was inside the body itself. Supplies of virus can be grown for experimental work, just as supplies of bacteria are grown on broth in a test-tube.

For growing polio virus Dr Enders used human tissue; soon this was replaced by tissue from the kidney of the common rhesus monkey. Kept alive in a suitable nourishing solution, this tissue would act as a host to the multiplying polio viruses.

Two years after Enders' discovery came another great step forward in polio research. Scientists confirmed that all the 100 or more known strains of polio virus could be grouped into three distinct types. Polio had this much in common with influenza, with its Type A and Type B viruses. All three of the polio viruses, named originally Brunhilde (Type 1), Lansing (Type 2), and Leon (Type 3), would cause the disease we recognize as polio. But each one generates antibodies in the blood which are specific in their activity; antibodies from a virus of one type will not protect the body against invasion by either of the other two types.

Until the many strains of polio virus were classified into these three types there was little hope of progress in developing vaccines that could be used for protection against the disease. A vaccine would be of real value only if it contained virus that could generate antibodies to destroy any invading polio virus. The recognition that all the many strains belonged to only three distinct types of virus meant that a vaccine was a practical proposition. It must contain viruses belonging to the three types; then it could produce antibodies that would deal with any strain of virus that made its way into the body.

By 1951 polio research had reached a critically important stage. It was known that all three types of virus could be cultivated in the laboratory on tissue taken from monkeys' kidneys. The way was open to the production of polio virus in quantity, even though monkey kidney is not so convenient or plentiful as the hen's egg used for growing influenza virus. Was it possible, then, to cultivate supplies of all three types of polio virus in monkey kidney, 'kill' the virus chemically, and use it as a vaccine to stimulate the natural defences of the body? That was what the polio scientists determined to find out.

Meanwhile, as all this research on the virus itself had been going on, doctors had been finding out something of the way in which the virus carried out its attack.

Post-mortem examinations showed that polio victims have virus in the spinal cord and in the brain. Also, infected people were found to excrete virus without necessarily showing symptoms of polio at all. They may have supplies of virus in various parts of the alimentary tract— in the throat or bowels, for example—and yet suffer no ill-effects.

This phenomenon, so striking in the case of polio, indicates that virus can be much more widespread during an epidemic than the casualties would indicate. As with 'flu, only a small proportion of people infected with polio will actually develop the severe disease. Many cases suffer only a mild reaction, similar to an ordinary cold. Others will have no symptoms at all, though they are capable of infecting others.

The wide dissemination of polio virus is now well established. Poliomyelitis is a common and natural human infection which is always with us. So far as we know man is the only animal affected naturally by the disease; monkeys and chimpanzees can be infected artificially, and the viruses can be persuaded to grow in mice and other rodents.

Whenever there is an epidemic of polio, virus can be detected in the sewage of the epidemic district. Flies are known to carry the virus, but it is not known exactly what part they play in spreading the disease.

It seems most likely that the virus is passed from one person to another by direct infection, through droplets in the breath or in the case of children by hand to mouth. The need for scrupulous cleanliness on the part of children at times of serious epidemics is self-evident.

To add to the problems of studying polio, it is no easy matter for the doctor to identify the disease. Many cases are almost indistinguishable from less serious infections. And positive identification of the virus itself taken from a suspect was, until recently, a tedious and costly proceeding. The sample had to be injected into monkeys and its effect studied.

Injected into the brain of a monkey, polio virus multiplies as it does inside a human being. After a few days the animal begins to develop a fever and loses the use of its limbs.

These symptoms are sufficient to show that a sample of spinal fluid from a patient may contain the polio virus. But to clinch the matter it is necessary to look for microscopic changes in the monkey's brain and spinal cord. Also, if the monkeys survive, polio antibodies are found in the blood serum.

This comparatively lengthy business made it difficult for doctors to follow the course of polio epidemics, and for many years it slowed up our study of the disease. But by 1955 Dr Mary Godenne and John T. Riordan, of Yale University School of Medicine, had developed a quick technique which enables a doctor to diagnose polio in a sick child that does not have symptoms of paralysis. The method combines the isolation of virus by tissue culture and its response to antibodies. Live monkeys are no longer needed.

When the polio virus has made its way into the body it moves towards the spinal cord and the brain. Here, in the cells of the central nervous system, it makes its home. And it is by multiplying inside these cells that the polio virus can cause paralysis.

All the voluntary movements of the human body, by means of which, for example, we use our arms and legs, are controlled by impulses sent along the nerves from cells in the central region of the spinal cord. These are the cells that pass on the final messages to the muscles. And it is in these 'motor' cells that polio virus is able to multiply particularly easily.

As it multiplies the virus damages the cells, and may destroy them completely. As these cells are irreplaceable, destruction caused by polio virus cannot be repaired. If sufficient cells have been destroyed in any region the muscles that they serve will have no controlling centre left. Paralysis is the result, and it is permanent. If the damage to the cells has not been too severe the cells can recover; in such cases control of the muscles can be restored.

The site of paralysis depends upon the position of the nerve-cells that are affected by the virus. The arm muscles are controlled by cells at the top of the spinal cord, and the legs by cells a foot or so lower down. Both of these nerve centres are favoured by the attacking polio virus. When the virus concentrates on the bulb at the base of the brain it affects the muscles controlling swallowing and speech; this type of paralysis is often fatal.

Much of the research on polio during recent years has

been directed towards following the route of the virus in the human body. Examination of people who have died of polio have shown that there is virus, as expected, in the nerve cells controlling muscular movements. But there is no virus in the nerves themselves, nor in the paralysed muscles. There is none in the blood nor in the main organs of the body.

Apart from the central nervous system, only one other place seems to harbour virus; this is the alimentary tract— the food-carrying system of the body. Virus is present in the throat and in the intestine walls, and in the contents of the digestive system.

Quite recently Dr David Bodian, of Johns Hopkins University, Baltimore, discovered what is believed to be the primary site of the polio infection. Virus was found to be multiplying in the tonsils and in lymph glands in the small intestine of chimpanzees exposed to infection. From these sites the virus made its way into the blood and then into the nervous system.

As virus multiplies in the tonsils antibodies are being generated by the bloodstream. If these antibodies are in sufficient strength by the time the virus is released into the blood the virus is overcome before it reaches the nervous system. No damage is done. But if the virus reaches its goal it may make its way towards the spinal cord and damage the motor nerve cells.

In human polio multiplication of the virus takes place for two or three days inside the nerve cells. During this time the natural defences of the body are in action and antibodies are being produced together with increased supplies of white blood cells to help in clearing up the bits and pieces left behind by the invasion.

If all goes well the antibodies overcome the virus and get rid of the infection within a week or two. Whether the virus has resulted in a severe disease or a sub-clinical attack, these antibodies remain as protection against subsequent attack by a similar strain of virus.

Even if the virus has made its way successfully into the nervous system it does not necessarily cause paralysis. Everything depends upon the amount of damage it is able to do before being overcome by the natural defences of the body. The result may be little more than a headache or a stiffness in the muscles of the neck.

Although we cannot yet defend ourselves against infection by the polio virus, we can do much to minimize the damage that is caused. There is plenty of evidence that over-exertion tends to encourage the polio virus multiplying in the nerve cells that control the muscles involved. Children showing the slightest sign of being off-colour during a polio epidemic should be made to rest. Also the discovery that polio virus makes its initial attack through the tonsils has confirmed what doctors had long suspected —removal of the tonsils during an epidemic of polio increases the likelihood of infection.

6

Protection against Polio

WITH our present understanding of polio we can see how the disease has been increasing in severity from year to year. Until a century or so ago people lived such an unhygienic life that any child would almost certainly be infected by the widespread polio virus during infancy. Protected for a month or two by antibodies passed on by its mother, the young baby would throw off the infection without suffering any harm. And by the time it was a year or two old it would have collected a concentration of antibodies in its bloodstream sufficient to cope with attack by any of the three types of polio virus in later life.

For some reason that we do not yet understand the severity of a polio attack increases with the age of the victim. A young child infected with polio virus is less likely to suffer serious damage than a schoolchild; a schoolchild is less vulnerable than an adult.

Infection during infant years, therefore, caused only infrequent cases of paralysis. This was the 'infantile paralysis' recognized in Britain during the eighteenth century.

As sanitation and housing conditions improved the chances of infection during infancy grew less. Children might well reach school age before being infected with a polio virus. Inevitably the time would come when the virus made its attack. And when it did, the child did not possess the antibodies that would provide a natural defence.

So, by the end of the nineteenth century, polio was becoming noticeable in some countries as an epidemic that affected children a few years old. The proportion of paralytic cases had increased as the severity became greater with advancing age. The disease which caused sporadic but infrequent cases of paralysis in infants had become an epidemic that brought paralysis to children approaching school age.

As civilization has pressed on with the job of making the world a cleaner and healthier place so have the attacks of polio become more widespread and severe. Adults are often affected, and the damage done is greater.

Even so the proportion of cases of polio that suffer any permanent harm is comparatively small. Out of every 100 people who are infected 66 will recover completely, 18 will suffer slight after effects, 10 will be crippled, and 6 will die. These figures are approximate, but are typical of many epidemics.

In spite of the delaying effect of modern living conditions on the spread of polio virus, few people will have escaped infection by the time they reach adulthood. Most will have fought off the virus attack without suffering any ill effects at all, or will have had only a very mild illness. But in the course of overcoming the disease they will have charged their blood with antibodies, and will have a natural protection that may last for the rest of their lives.

In the United States, where polio has done more damage than in any other country, almost every adult carries antibodies against all three strains of polio virus in the blood. Few have escaped infection by the three viruses during youth. They have reached the haven of adulthood and need fear the polio virus no longer.

This situation is common in densely-populated, modern communities. But in isolated districts people may well avoid infection by one or all of the polio viruses until comparatively late in life. If infection should then be introduced from outside polio can spread like wildfire, with tragic results.

The effect of different degrees of immunization is well shown by recent experiences of polio in island communities.

In 1943 the Mediterranean island of Malta suffered an epidemic of polio soon after the raising of the wartime siege. The outbreak of clinical disease was restricted almost entirely to the youngest children of the island. Nine out of ten of the victims were under five years of age. More than half of these were under two years of age.

On St Helena, on the other hand, an epidemic of polio struck swiftly and suddenly at young and old alike. Both attacks were severe, indicating that a virulent type of virus was involved. But why such a difference in the age range of victims between the two islands?

The answer lies in the health history of Malta as compared with that of St Helena. Malta has had polio cases cropping up among its children for as long as records have been kept. Most children in Malta, therefore, become infected in early life. A few of them suffer actual clinical disease. The remaining children develop an immunity which is strengthened as the years pass by subsequent infections.

So, when a virulent virus appears in 1943 it is the young children who are affected by it most. The adults and older children carry their own protection with them in their bloodstream.

In St Helena the story is a different one. Here there had been no polio for more than twenty years. By being isolated from the virus through geographical conditions the inhabitants were denying themselves the opportunity of building up their antibody protection. When the virus *did* strike it found itself free to roam among children and young adults, with devastating results.

The Eskimo population on the north-west shore of Hudson's Bay suffered a similar fate in the winter of 1948-49. Here the virus struck violently against young and old alike. Though adequate medical records do not exist for these people, it seems certain that they suffered by having no natural antibody protection in their blood. The virus could therefore carry infection to every age group of the community.

Recently John R. Paul, of Yale University, showed that antibodies for one of the polio viruses were absent from the blood of all people younger than twenty in a group of Alaskan Eskimos. Older Eskimos did possess these antibodies. And the last epidemic of polio occurred exactly twenty years previously. A striking proof of the way in which the natural body defences are developed.

In the United States and in Western European countries an immense research effort is now being made to find out how we can best protect ourselves against the attack of polio. We can assume that most people will be carrying their own antibodies by the time they reach their twenties; adults are therefore able to look after themselves. But children and young adults, infected at increasingly later stages as our standards of public health improve, need help in meeting the attack of the polio virus.

This help can best be given by finding a way of stimulating antibody-protection artificially at an early age. If we can supply every child with antibodies against all three types of polio, we can be sure that the risk of paralysis is lessened when, as is certain, the child is infected during later life.

One way of providing this protection is to inject the antibodies themselves. This we can do by collecting blood from adults who are carrying all three types of antibody. In the serum of this blood, polio antibodies form part of the substance known as gamma globulin. If we inject supplies of gamma globulin into a child we can be sure of providing it with a ration of antibodies effective against all three types of polio virus.

In 1953 a mass experiment was carried out in parts of Utah, Texas, and Iowa to test the effect of giving children gamma-globulin injections as protection against polio.

FOOT-AND-MOUTH DISEASE VIRUS

This is cultivated for making protective vaccine on ox-tongues, which are first cleansed and sterilized.

Photo Dr H. S. Frenkel, Amsterdam

VIRUS GROWING IN EGGS

Eggs are here being inoculated with rabies virus.

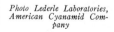

Photo Lederle Laboratories, American Cyanamid Company

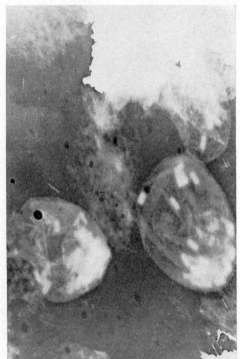

INSECT VIRUSES

(*Left*) Rod-shaped polyhedral virus from the caterpillar of the privet hawk moth. Virus rods from dissolved crystals are seen singly and in bundles. (×11,000)

(*Right*) Rod-shaped virus from the caterpillar of the muslin moth. (×11,000).

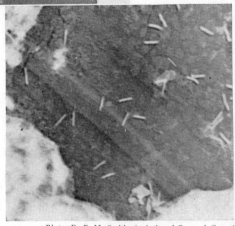

Photos Dr F. M. Smith, Agricultural Research Council

More than 250,000 children were inoculated with five million cubic centimetres of gamma globulin extracted from the blood of adults. The results were inconclusive, although it has been claimed that the antibodies in the gamma globulin conferred a temporary protection against polio, lasting up to two months.

This use of gamma globulin may prove to be a valuable emergency measure against polio, but it can hardly be regarded as a practical long-term proposition. To provide a long-lasting and reliable protection we must resort once again to the stimulation of the body's own defences. We must inject a vaccine that can induce the body to manufacture its own supplies of antibodies.

On the face of it the development of a vaccine for protection against polio should be a relatively straightforward job. We can adopt either of two alternative processes. We can inject a vaccine made from mild strains of the three types of polio virus, or we can inject three virulent strains which have been killed by chemical treatment before injection.

Unfortunately the job of producing a polio vaccine is very much more difficult in practice than in theory. There are, for example, no convenient 'natural' mild viruses of polio comparable with the cowpox or vaccinia viruses that we use against smallpox.

There is no immediate prospect of using living polio viruses for protection in this way. But the use of vaccines made from 'dead' polio virus is another matter. Since 1954 a vaccine of this type has been under examination in the United States, Canada, and some European countries.

The development of this vaccine was achieved by Dr Jonas E. Salk, of the University of Pittsburgh. It was the culmination of seventeen years of research encouraged by the National Foundation for Infantile Paralysis.

Two fundamental discoveries made the Salk polio vaccine possible. One was the discovery by Dr John Enders in 1949 that polio virus could be grown in cultures of living non-nervous tissue taken from monkeys. This was a technique that could be used on a large scale for making the immense quantity of virus that would be needed for mass vaccination.

The second great step forward was the realization, in 1951, that all strains of polio virus could be classified into three types; every strain in each of the types would produce antibodies effective against all the other strains of this type.

Salk realized that these two discoveries opened the way to the production of a polio vaccine. He set to work immediately, testing out systematically the various monkey tissues in which the virus grew. He confirmed that the kidney was the best.

Salk and his colleagues grew the tissue cells in many different sorts of ' broth,' settling eventually on one that contained some sixty-two ingredients, balanced delicately and precisely to give the growing tissue everything it needed. The most difficult problem of all was to find a way of 'killing' the virus so that it was safe for use as a vaccine. The virus must not be so damaged that it did not stimulate production of the appropriate antibodies. Yet it had to be well and truly inactivated to ensure that it could not cause disease when it was injected into man.

Dr Salk devised a method of killing his viruses chemically with formaldehyde. By the early summer of 1952 he had made many experimental vaccines by growing polio virus in cultures of living tissue. Killed with formaldehyde, the virus could be injected into monkeys without harming the animals. Yet the monkeys developed antibodies in their blood which protected them against subsequent infection by a dangerous living polio virus.

Salk tested his vaccine rigorously, and showed that it was entirely safe in animals; the stage was set for testing it on human beings. Despite every precaution that was taken in making the vaccine, nobody could be absolutely sure that it was harmless.

The first experiments with Salk's vaccine were therefore made on people who were known to have recovered from polio. They would not show any outward signs of infection, but the effectiveness of the vaccine could be assessed by measuring the antibody-level of the blood. Sure enough, vaccination raised the concentration of polio antibodies; the 'dead' virus in the vaccine was stimulating the natural body defences as expected. The time had come to think in terms of mass-inoculation of children on a national scale.

Plans were made for the production of Salk vaccine in the quantities that would be needed for vaccinating millions of children. The practical difficulties involved were staggering. Virus was to be grown in one of the strangest industrial raw materials of all time—living tissue from monkeys' kidneys. And the virus from which the vaccine would be made was one of the most dangerous and infective disease-producing organisms known.

But by 1954 vaccine was being produced in quantity sufficient to carry out the first large-scale vaccinations. From the Philippines and from India monkeys were being flown in their thousands every month to special farms in the United States. After a careful health-check they were dispatched to vaccine factories to provide living-quarters in which the polio virus would multiply.

Three types of virus were grown; after being killed with formaldehyde they were mixed to form the vaccine. Then, for weeks, each batch of vaccine went through a series of rigorous tests to ensure that it was entirely safe for injection into human beings.

During the summer of 1954 the cherry-red Salk vaccine was injected into school children in 217 selected areas of the United States and in three districts in Canada and one in Finland.

Altogether 1,840,000 children took part in this greatest medical experiment in history. Salk vaccine was given to 440,000 of them and an injection of harmless liquid to 210,000.

Each child had a record card on which information and progress details were recorded. Altogether 144 million separate items of information were collected during the course of the experiment. Every item was checked twice to ensure that it was correct.

Twenty-seven laboratories in the United States and in Canada took part in the immense experiment, testing blood from 40,000 children in order to assess the changing antibody-level.

The Salk vaccine was estimated to be 80–90 per cent. effective as a result of the 1954 experiment. In all but a few cases it raised the level of polio antibodies in the blood in such a way as to protect the child against infection. And it did this without causing major side-effects.

Only four children in every 1000 vaccinated suffered minor reactions such as faintness, sickness, or dizziness. Only four in every 100,000 had a major reaction such as a high fever, severe pains in arms and legs, and severe rash.

The actual number of cases of polio was lower among the inoculated children than in those who had not been given any vaccine. In the period June to December 1954 there were only a third to a quarter as many paralysis cases in inoculated children as there were in unprotected children. The vaccine was most effective in children aged seven, eight, and nine. The youngest children taking part in the experiment, aged six years, were less well protected by the vaccine.

There was no doubt, therefore, on the basis of the 1954 experiment that the Salk vaccine was able to give a useful degree of protection against polio. The trials did not show how long the protection would last.

In 1955 mass vaccination continued on an even greater scale, and by August of that year eight million children had been vaccinated in the United States, Canada, and Denmark.

The full effect of these vaccinations on the actual course of polio epidemics cannot be thoroughly assessed for several years. Polio fluctuates from season to season and the low 1955 figure in the United States could well have been caused by a natural lull in the polio cycle. It was higher, for example, than the 1950 and 1951 figures.

The speed with which these mass inoculations were organized and the scale on which they were carried out stirred up a great deal of criticism in the United States. On the one hand, public opinion favoured any measure which would call a halt to polio epidemics, which are increasing in severity from year to year. On the other hand, many scientists and doctors were horrified at the idea of injecting potentially dangerous vaccines into millions of children before they had been assessed gradually over several years.

The results of the 1954 trials, however, were sufficient to show that the Salk vaccine in the form then used was perfectly safe. It certainly gave a useful, though not 100 per cent., protection against polio.

During the 1955 trials some 100 cases of polio occurred among the millions of children who were inoculated with Salk vaccine. This in itself was not unexpected, as the vaccine does not protect every child that receives it. But it was found that many of these cases had occurred in children who received vaccine made by one particular laboratory. Immediately this raised a suspicion that the virus in the vaccine was not as 'dead' as it ought to be. A careful investigation took place, and the methods of preparation and testing of the virus were overhauled.

The Medical Research Council in Britain were kept fully informed of progress in the United States polio experiments. Plans were made to produce the Salk vaccine in sufficient quantity for preliminary trials on animals. But the polio problem in Britain is not the same as that in the United States; it was believed that experiments should be made only with the greatest caution after finding out as much as possible about the disease itself.

In the United States polio epidemics have been recurring regularly since the early 1900's, and the severity of

the disease has been increasing. The need for rapid action
in polio research has become self-evident. But in Britain
polio epidemics are a comparatively recent experience. We
regard polio almost as a post-World War II disease. The
epidemics of 1947, 1949, and 1950 were more widespread
than any we had known before the War.

Only in recent years have we begun to develop a sense
of urgency about polio. We see how polio has increased its
threat year by year in the United States and presume that
it is going to repeat the performance in Britain.

Already we can detect the changing pattern of polio
attack in Britain. In the early years of the present century
polio did most of its damage to children under the age of
four years. But since 1938 most of the serious cases have
been in older children and young adults. In post-World
War II epidemics only a third of the polio victims were
under the age of five. Another third were between five and
fourteen, and the remaining third fifteen years old or more.

This trend is similar to that which has taken place in the
United States and in Scandinavian countries, where improved standards of living have postponed the inevitable
polio infection into later years. There is no reason to doubt
that in Britain also this trend will be marked by epidemics that become more serious from year to year.

It was with this in mind that the Medical Research
Council planned its vaccine experiments in Britain. As a
preliminary it was essential to 'map' the distribution of
infection in British children, so that vaccination could be
carried out at the most effective age. Blood tests of children began in May 1955, and laboratories were adapted to
carry out the examination of the samples taken from
thousands of children. Each sample would show the level
of polio antibodies in the child from which the blood was
taken. This, in turn, would indicate whether the child had
been infected by any of the three types of polio virus in
the past.

Progress in these early experiments was slow. The polio

cases occurring during the 1955 mass inoculation in the
United States stressed the need for taking every precaution in preparing the vaccine. During this same year the
Government of India banned the export of monkeys which
were needed for testing the safety of vaccines. And the
knowledge that the act of vaccination may increase the
chances of paralysis in a child already infected with polio
raised difficulties in timing a vaccination programme.

Meanwhile research on the vaccine itself has been making headway. Some experts believe that a better vaccine
can be made by using mild strains of polio virus instead of
the 'killed' virus used for the Salk vaccine. These living
viruses could be taken as a pill instead of an injection.
They would possibly give a more lasting protection than
the dead viruses in the Salk vaccine.

It is now possible to change the personality of the three
polio viruses by growing them in special living tissues.
Viruses have been made in this way which could safely be
given to children. They would cause only a harmless form
of polio, comparable with the mild disease we get from a
vaccination against smallpox.

But viruses are shifty creatures; they can undergo mutation so easily, changing from a harmless strain to a virulent,
killing micro-organism. Mass experiments with a living
polio virus, no matter how docile it might appear to be,
would carry a heavy load of responsibility.

At the present time the Salk-type vaccine seems to offer
the greatest hope of giving us a worth-while protection
against polio. Growing the virus on the living tissue of a
monkey kidney is not an ideal manufacturing technique.
But it can be done in such a way as to provide material
for vaccinating millions of children in a season. Moreover
new and more plentiful sources of living tissue have been
found. In 1955 it was discovered that all three types of
polio virus will grow in human afterbirth tissue. The
maternity hospital may in future provide vaccine raw
material that formerly came from the monkey.

In common with other viruses, the polio virus cannot be destroyed in the body with the help of any of our modern drugs. Yet there is a possibility that we can encourage the cells of the nervous system to overcome the virus that is threatening to destroy them. As our knowledge of cell-metabolism increases we are discovering that we can influence the growth of viruses by withholding some of their essential needs. Mice fed on a diet deficient in some of the B vitamins, for example, have been found less vulnerable to attack by polio virus.

7

The Common Cold

THE difficulties facing the virus scientist have been well enough established in the case of influenza, poliomyelitis, and other diseases. But they increase alarmingly when we come to the common cold.

As an economic threat, the common cold is comparable with influenza. Nobody knows how much lost working time the cold costs us every year. In Britain alone it has been estimated at 40 million working days.

The common cold, like influenza, is not in general a 'killing' disease. Its effects are distressing and annoying rather than dangerous, so that there has been no dramatic urge to find a way of protecting ourselves as in the case of diseases like smallpox or yellow fever. It is in fact only within the last few years that we have really settled down to make a serious study of the common cold at all.

In Britain research began in 1946. Under the direction of Dr C. H. Andrewes, head of the bacteriology and virus research at the National Institute for Medical Research in London, a Common Cold Research Unit was established with headquarters at Harvard Hospital, Salisbury. Here, in buildings presented to the Ministry of Health by the Harvard Medical School, research on the common cold has been carried out.

Although a great deal has been found out about the disease since 1946, many problems connected with the common cold have yet to be solved.

One thing is now certain. Colds are caused by a virus.

Nasal secretions taken from people suffering from colds can be filtered to remove all bacteria. These clear 'germ-free' liquids will infect susceptible people with colds when dropped into their nostrils. If secretions are taken from the noses of the new victims the same thing can be done again, and again the cold can be passed on. In this way it is possible to transmit a cold from one person to another almost any number of times. Yet there is no germ to be seen in the nasal washings that pass on the cold. The infective agent must be a virus.

Until 1954 nobody had any idea what the common cold virus looked like. But in that year electron-microscope photographs of one strain of the common cold virus were taken by scientists from the Walter Reed Army Hospital, in Washington, and from the University of Maryland. The virus resembles a midget billiard ball about three-millionths of an inch in diameter.

Prior to this scientists at the Common Cold Research Unit in Salisbury had estimated the size of the virus without even seeing it at all. Fluids containing the virus were filtered through collodion diaphragms pierced by pores of a known size. By testing the fluid after it had filtered through these diaphragms the common cold researchers were able to find how small the pores must be to hold the virus back. When the holes were only 120-millionths of an inch across there was little loss of potency. And with holes only half this size the fluid was still infective.

From these experiments it was deduced that the common cold virus was one of the smaller viruses—about the same size as that of yellow fever, which is some 25 millimicrons[1] in diameter. It was much smaller than the influenza virus.

Research on the Common Cold has not progressed at anything like the rate of research on influenza. The reason for this lies mainly in the fact that we have no convenient,

[1] The millimicron is a unit of size that is used in measuring viruses; it is one-millionth of a millimetre—about one-25-millionth of an inch.

simple host in which the cold virus can be cultivated experimentally. Apart from human beings only chimpanzees appear to be able to catch colds. But chimpanzees cost more than a hundred pounds apiece, and they die of pneumonia with disturbing ease. Chimpanzees are virtually useless as experimental animals. When the Common Cold Research Unit was set up at Salisbury in 1946 there was no alternative but to use man himself as the ' guinea pig.'

There were plenty of problems to be solved. How does the virus pass from one person to another? Why do some people catch cold more easily than others? What are the conditions that make us susceptible to colds? Can a cold vaccine be made?

The basic need of any research of this sort is always to find a simple reliable test that will detect the presence of virus. If there is a convenient laboratory animal that is susceptible to infection by the virus testing is comparatively easy. A sample suspected of containing the virus is injected into a few animals and in due course they are examined to see if the virus has multiplied inside them. But in the case of the common cold testing was no easy matter. Human beings cannot be kept in cages away from stray infections by natural viruses. Nor can we keep a supply of tame human beings for the sole purpose of testing for the common cold. Somehow or other arrangements must be made for using a succession of volunteers who are prepared to act as guinea pigs for a short time before returning to their normal work.

Research at the Harvard Hospital at Salisbury was planned on this basis. Six huts were each divided into two separate flats, each flat being able to house a pair of volunteers. The hospital can therefore handle twenty-four experimental human beings at a time.

When the Unit was ready to start work in 1947 appeals were made in the British Press and over the radio for people between the ages of eighteen and forty who would be willing to spend a fortnight at the hospital. Since then volunteers have been passing through at a rate of about 500 a year.

When the volunteers arrive at Salisbury station they are taken to the hospital and examined immediately to see whether they have a cold. If a volunteer has come without bringing a friend he is paired off with a partner, and the two volunteers take up residence in one of the flats. Here they remain for a fortnight in isolation. They will meet nobody but the carefully gowned and masked doctor and matron who make a daily visit. Food is brought three times a day and left in Thermos flasks outside the door.

To help in passing the time each flat is provided with a radio, and there are table tennis and other games. Each pair of volunteers is allowed to go out for walks, but they must keep away from any contact with other people.

For the first three days the volunteers are kept under observation to see if colds develop naturally. If not, the ' guinea pigs ' are regarded as being cold-free, and the experiments can begin.

Each volunteer is inoculated with one of three possible solutions. Some receive nasal secretions known from past experience to be infective. Others receive a harmless salt solution. And the rest are given an inoculation with an experimental solution which is being tested for cold virus.

To make the inoculation the patient lies with his head held back and the liquid is dropped into his nostrils. Nobody—not even the doctor giving the inoculation—knows at the time which type of liquid is being given. There is therefore no chance of any involuntary bias in the opinions of either doctor or volunteer.

For the next ten days the volunteers are left to enjoy their dose of virus or salt. Every day they are visited by the doctor and matron.

Finally, after ten days, the volunteers return home, leaving behind them a little bit of additional information about the virus of the common cold.

By careful control and inspection these human volunteers can be used effectively in this way as experimental animals. They are not as cheap, nor are they as expendable, as mice or eggs. But in the case of the common cold they are the only convenient host for the virus. They can tell the research workers whether a test solution contains cold virus or not.

The volunteers who are inoculated with salt solution normally remain free of colds throughout the period of the test, thus providing a control which guarantees that the precautions taken against accidental infection are adequate.

One peculiar feature of these common cold researches has been the fact that only about half of the volunteers receiving virus will actually develop colds. Many of the others will show signs of a cold developing, but this will clear away in a matter of one or two days before maturing properly. Some factor which is not yet understood is able to overcome infection in every other person, so that in assessing the infectiveness of an inoculation fluid this 50 per cent. susceptibility has to be taken into account.

The protection may be due to normal antibody protection left by previous cold infections, but experience has shown that such protection in the case of the common cold is transient. People can catch a series of colds with only a short interval of time between each. The antibodies—if they are in fact responsible for protection—seem to disappear very quickly from the blood.

Since the cold researches began many attempts have been made to cultivate the cold virus in animals other than human beings. Squirrels, hedgehogs, pigs, kittens, ferrets, mice—these and many others have been tried without success.

In America research workers have claimed to be able to grow cold virus in hens' eggs by a technique similar to that used for cultivating influenza virus. But in England these results have not been duplicated, possibly because a

different strain of virus is used. The strain used by Dr
Norman Topping and Dr Leon T. Atlas, at the United
States National Institute of Health, called V14 A, is not
the same strain of virus as that which is being studied at
Salisbury.

One of the most unexpected discoveries made during
common cold research has been the effect of chilling on a
person's susceptibility to colds. Every grandma knows that
colds are caused by wet feet or sitting in draughts. It is an
accepted tradition in most parts of the world that chilling
the body in one way or another will bring on a cold. It was
thought that this may have some bearing on the 50 per
cent. 'take' of the virus in the infection of volunteers, so
experiments were carried out to examine the effect of chilling on susceptibility. The results were surprising.

Volunteers were given hot baths and left to stand in
draughty passages. They went for walks in the rain and
sat about in damp clothes. They wore wet socks. And yet
they did not catch cold any more easily than volunteers
living under normal conditions.

The entire question of susceptibility to colds is still
wrapped in mystery, and it seems probable that many factors are involved. Age has been found to have little effect,
at least between eighteen and forty. Women catch cold
more easily than men; this may be due to slight differences
in the chemistry of the female body.

The antibody situation in the case of colds is only
sketchily understood. We do not know why protection
lasts for so short a time.

Like the influenza virus, the virus of the common cold
probably makes its attack on the cells which line the respiratory passages. And, as in the case of 'flu, the virus is
therefore able to settle down without being attacked by a
concentration of antibodies in the bloodstream, even if
they are there.

No drugs yet known can tackle the common cold virus
directly inside the body. As with other viruses, our

defences are essentially those of the body itself. So-called cold cures examined objectively under controlled conditions have been found ineffective. The fact that the body can so often nip a cold in the bud itself offers fertile ground for cold-cure salesmanship. Too often credit is given to a cold-cure for what the body itself has done.

As in the case of any other disease, many things will help to relieve the unpleasant effects of colds and comfort the victim. But they will do little more than that. Even the antihistamine drugs, which were widely acclaimed as cold-cures during 1949, have failed to stand up to tests carried out under properly controlled conditions. They are useful against certain allergic conditions such as hay-fever, but not, apparently, against the common cold.

Prevention, as with most diseases, is better than cure in the case of the common cold. We do not know why some people are hypersensitive to the virus and will catch a cold more easily than others. But we *do* know that the virus is spread by droplet infection through the air.

A sneeze by some one with a cold will fill the air in a room with hundreds of thousands of floating droplets of moisture that do not settle out for an hour or more. These droplets can carry cold virus from one person to another. And if he happens to be susceptible the victim will catch a cold.

Even when these droplets settle they can dry on the floor or on our clothing and then be redispersed as dust.

In crowded places when colds are about the air itself can be cleared of most of its germs to keep down epidemics. Ventilation will carry off infected droplets and replace the infected air by clean fresh air. Where conditions permit, the air can be disinfected by sprays or by ultra-violet light.

But in spite of these precautions, it is impossible to control the spread of virus for twenty-four hours of every day. We are not even certain about the importance of the role of airborne infection as compared with other routes.

An experiment carried out at Salisbury showed how effectively the common cold virus can be spread by infected mucus on the hands. One of the volunteers was equipped with an artificial dribbly nose. This consisted of a small tank from which a tube led to the nose. Liquid from the tank was allowed to run slowly through the tube at a rate similar to that at which a nose 'runs' during a heavy cold.

The liquid in the artificial runny nose contained a fluorescent dye which would glow vividly in ultra-violet light.

The volunteer looked after his artificial nose exactly as he would have treated it during a natural cold. He blew his nose when necessary, using his handkerchief to keep the 'mucus' under control. After four hours had been spent in normal routine activities an ultra-violet lamp was switched on to show how the 'mucus' had been distributed. The dye fluoresced brightly on the face and hands of the volunteer; it was all over his clothes and scattered about the furniture he had been using. It had even reached the food on the table.

There seems little doubt that the cold virus spreads by droplet infection and also by direct contact with people suffering from a cold. But there are apparently many factors that influence the way in which a cold is passed from one person to another. Nobody yet knows why only 50 per cent. of the volunteers deliberately injected with virus develop a cold. Nor do we understand how susceptibility is affected by periods of complete isolation.

It is a well known fact that Arctic explorers do not suffer from colds. When little bands of people are cut off in this way from contact with civilization the cold virus seems to disappear. Even though explorers may take colds with them when they leave for polar regions, the virus cannot remain alive and active for very long. Once contact is re-made with civilization, however, the explorer finds himself being attacked again by the common cold virus. His avoidance of colds has left him unusually susceptible to infection, and he catches cold more readily than the normal person.

This effect of isolation was studied by the Common Cold Unit in an attempt to throw some light on the way in which the virus is spread about. An uninhabited island off the coast of Scotland was ‘ borrowed ’ from the Duke of Sutherland, and twelve volunteer students were marooned there during the summer of 1950.

For the first ten weeks the twelve students lived together, after which they divided up into three separate groups of four. Each party lived in its own third of the island. One of the parties was then visited by two scientists from the mainland in the expectation that the newcomers would pass on common cold virus to the extra-susceptible students who had been free of colds for several weeks. But nothing happened.

Then six people were sent to the island after being deliberately infected with cold virus from the hospital at Salisbury. They spent three hours in a room normally used by one of the parties of students, moving about and handling cups and plates and other everyday equipment to make sure that everything was liberally contaminated with infected secretions. Then the visitors departed and the students returned.

The second party was given a different treatment. This time the visiting cold-carriers spent some hours in a room, separated from the students by a screen that allowed air to circulate freely from one part of the room to the other. The visitors chatted and sneezed, filling the air with a spray of fine droplets that floated through the screen.

Finally the third party of students looked after the visitors and lived in close contact with them in the normal way.

The object of these experiments was to try and assess the importance of different methods of transmitting cold virus from one person to another. Did the virus travel most efficiently in air, or was it handed on by contact with infected mucus?

The results were unexpected. None of the students caught a cold at all. In spite of the fact that their two and a half months' freedom from cold should have left them unusually susceptible, they were not infected by the virus.

This strange result was difficult to explain. Could it be due to the fact that the virus used for infecting the visitors was a pedigree strain from Salisbury?

To test this theory a crofter suffering from a natural cold was brought to the island from the mainland for a day. Soon three of the party of eight who came into contact with the crofter were suffering from colds. It seemed, therefore, that there must be some difference in 'catch-ability' between the pedigree virus used in the experiments of the Common Cold Research Unit and the 'wild' virus that causes colds in the world outside. Possibly the serene and special surroundings under which the virus lives in Salisbury have modified it in some way.

This sort of difficulty is characteristic of the research that has been going on at Salisbury since 1946. Everything is against the scientist who sets out to investigate the common cold. So many factors are involved in every aspect of research. The human guinea pigs are only 50 per cent. receptive to infection. Diagnosis is difficult. A cold cannot easily be characterized as any definite disease.

Yet progress is being made. The Salisbury scientists, in 1953, discovered a method of growing cold virus in living tissue in the laboratory. Cultures of human lung tissue were inoculated with secretions from the noses of volunteers with colds. The tissue cultures were fed with nutrient liquids, and every three days the cultures were diluted and transferred to new tubes. For more than a month this experiment continued until the original viruses supplied in the nasal secretions would have been diluted 100,000 times. Unless they had multiplied in the human lung tissue the culture liquid would no longer be infective.

Drops of the liquid were given to volunteers in the hospital at Salisbury. They duly developed colds, proving that at last, after seven years, the virus of the common cold had been cultivated successfully in the laboratory.

Just as the tissue-culture technique has given us a vaccine for defence against polio, so will this cultivation of cold virus open the way to the production of a vaccine against the common cold.

We know little as yet about the effects of environment on the development of colds. Why are colds commoner in winter than in summer? We do not know. It is not simply a question of temperature. Waves of colds, for example, spread across a country like the United States simultaneously from the Canadian border to the Gulf of Mexico. They do not begin in the colder areas and spread outward with the colder weather.

It is possible that sudden temperature changes have some effect, although the chilling experiments do not support this theory.

Can it be that cold weather works indirectly by tending to crowd people together during winter? If this is the cause of cold epidemics, why should colds not spread in crowded trains and buses in the summer months?

The virus of the common cold causes immense economic loss. In spite of the difficulties, research on the common cold must remain as an urgent problem for science.

For centuries past people have been pinning their faith on all sorts of treatments and medicines that they are convinced will cure a cold. In 1676 a British doctor writing in *Physick and Astrology* recommended a syrup made from garlic and brown sugar. By 1808 a Philadelphia surgeon was curing colds by giving his patients " frequent draughts of cold fluids, combined with nauseating emetics."

Nowadays we have cold ' cures ' that include sun lamps and cold baths, hot fruit juices in the morning and alcoholic refreshment at night, faith-healing and flannel underwear, laxatives and spinal corsets, yogi and yoghourt.

Many of these treatments will undoubtedly bring some relief by making the victim a little more comfortable as he sniffles his way through his cold. In that respect they are valuable. But so far as we can tell by careful scientific tests, none will really cure.

It seems likely that the most effective treatment for a cold will develop from some sort of vaccine that can stimulate our antibodies. Like the influenza virus, the virus of the common cold does not make its entry into the body through the bloodstream; even though there may be antibodies in the blood, they will not reach the virus in sufficient strength to attack it as it multiplies in the membranes of the respiratory passages.

Perhaps we shall find the answer to the common cold in vaccines that are brought into direct contact with the membranes in which the virus is settling down. We may be able to ' vaccinate ' ourselves by gargling with a suitable vaccine, or—as Dr Andrewes has suggested—by taking it as snuff.

8

Other Virus Diseases of Man

THOUGH viruses can, as we have seen, cause some of the most distressing of all human diseases, they are also responsible for many of the less severe diseases of childhood, and for minor afflictions such as warts and cold-sores.

Mumps, measles, and chicken-pox are all virus diseases. As in the case of more serious diseases, we must depend for our protection upon the mechanisms of the body itself.

In most civilized countries, where people are continually in contact with each other, virus diseases have ample opportunity to spread from one person to another. During schooldays children pick up infection by measles, mumps, and chicken-pox viruses. Once infected, the patient's blood becomes charged with antibodies and he is normally protected from further attack for the rest of his life. Like polio, these common virus diseases tend to become diseases of childhood. The virus is given an opportunity of attacking early, and adults carry their own protection with them in their bloodstreams.

When these common virus diseases are introduced into isolated communities they can become more serious and will often attack children and adults alike. As in the case of polio when it struck St Helena, the virus may find itself on virgin ground. The disease is new to the community. Adults do not carry antibodies in their blood, and they suffer as readily as the children.

Measles can be a serious disease under such conditions. Natives in a Pacific island, for example, may have been

isolated from contact with the measles virus for generations. The population would be too small and scattered to
enable the virus to support itself by attacking successive
generations. In the course of time the measles virus will
have died out in the island. A re-introduction of the virus
enables the disease to spread as an epidemic, often with
serious results.

The dangers inherent in this sort of isolation from
infection were brought home with tragic effect to many
Australian families during World War II. An epidemic of
German measles among young married couples led to congenital defects in many children born to mothers who had
the disease during pregnancy.

In Britain and other densely populated countries most
children are infected by the German measles virus during
school-days. The disease is a mild one and has no serious
after-effects. The antibodies generated by the attack are
usually able to guarantee protection for life against a
second attack.

In Australia there is no such likelihood of every child
coming into contact with a German measles virus during
school-days. Australia is a sparsely-populated country and
many people may well grow to adulthood without becoming infected by the range of viruses that assault the child
in a British school.

In 1937 an epidemic of German measles began in
Queensland, spreading from year to year until by 1940 and
1941 it was covering the country. The unusual thing about
this epidemic, from the point of view of people in more
densely-populated countries, was that it involved many
youngsters in their late teens, as well as children still at
school.

The explanation was a simple one. There had been no
epidemic of German measles in Australia since the early
1920's. For nearly twenty years children had grown up
without any antibodies in their blood to protect them
against the German measles virus. When an epidemic *did*

get under way the virus included all these young adults in its programme of infection.

In the normal way there was nothing to worry about unduly in this delayed infection by German measles. Even in the adult it was not regarded as a dangerous disease.

In 1941 an Australian doctor, N. M. Gregg, became concerned at the number of babies who were being brought to him suffering from congenital eye defects. These babies had been born with one or both of the eye lenses less transparent than in the normal eye.

This was an unusual defect, and its sudden arrival prompted Dr Gregg to enquire into the pregnancy history of the mother of every afflicted child. He found that the mothers had suffered an attack of German measles during the early months of their pregnancies.

Soon it was found that other defects in new-born children could be related to German measles in the same way. Babies were often under-developed and suffered from the heart disease that gives them the name 'blue babies.' They were often deaf.

At first doctors in other countries were reluctant to believe that German measles could, in fact, be responsible for these congenital defects in Australian babies. Yet it was established that German measles was indeed to blame. The effect of the disease during pregnancy had not been appreciated before, as young girls in highly-populated countries were almost invariably infected during early childhood. Australia was suffering the consequences of her many years of freedom from German measles epidemics.

The discovery that German measles can have such disastrous after-effects during pregnancy has stimulated research on the disease. German measles had always been accepted as one of those harmless diseases that every child could expect to get during school-days. As like as not the symptoms would be so mild that the disease would go on its way unnoticed.

But now, the virus of German measles has shown that in

special circumstances it can cripple and maim as tragically as polio. It can no longer be accepted with the tolerance that we showed to it before.

Unfortunately German measles is an awkward disease to study. The virus is as unco-operative as the virus of the common cold. So far as we know, it will grow only inside the human being and possibly in monkeys.

The limitations set by the use of human beings as experimental animals are narrowed even more by the fact that volunteers can serve only once. They must not have had German measles previously. And once they have had an experimental dose they cannot get another one.

What this means in practice is that we cannot set up a German Measles Research Unit similar to that which is investigating the common cold. First we shall have to find a substitute for the human experimental animal, and use this as the basis for research.

Investigations have now shown that the danger from German measles is confined to the first four months of pregnancy. The risk to the unborn child is greatest during the second month and slightly less during the third.

At present there is little that can be done to prevent the German measles virus doing its damage if the mother is attacked. But experiments have shown that it is possible to protect the mother during the danger period by providing antibodies from the blood of people who have had the disease. Gamma globulin injections containing these antibodies enable the mother to resist the attack of German measles virus until the first few months of pregnancy have passed.

The simplest and most effective way of protecting the young mother against these effects of German measles is, of course, to make sure that she has had the disease during childhood. Many schoolgirls in Australia have been infected deliberately with German measles virus in this way.

One of the commonest of all of the human virus diseases is that which causes cold sores on our mouths and lips.

This widespread but trivial disease is found in every country in the world. There is no danger in the disease, nor does it cause any undue economic loss. But in spite of this the virus that causes cold sores has been the subject of a great deal of research. It is an unusually interesting virus, which has established a unique relationship with its human host.

The disease that causes these cold sores is more properly known as *herpes simplex*. It is an 'old' disease, which has been causing cold sores on human lips ever since man lived in caves and killed his dinner with a club. During this long association the virus of *herpes simplex* has come to an amicable arrangement with man; it has learned to live permanently inside its host, even though the blood is charged with antibodies that can destroy it.

Cold sores can appear with distressing regularity on a person's lips. Some people are obviously susceptible to the sores; others go through life without getting cold sores under any circumstances.

As long ago as 1912 it was shown that the fluid in a *herpes simplex* sore was highly infective. Filtered to remove bacteria, it would cause a disease in rabbits which was often fatal. Everything pointed to the fact that *herpes simplex* was a virus disease.

Yet in spite of this, the disease itself did not behave as though it was an infection passed from one person to another. People with cold sores do not infect other adults with the disease.

Also it is well known that cold sores are brought on by all sorts of different circumstances. Often they will appear as a result of too much sunshine or a bitter wind. They arrive as part and parcel of internal upsets; many people get a crop of cold sores whenever they have a cold or 'flu.

This recurrence of cold sores in an individual is not a result of any obvious infection from outside. People do not 'catch' cold sores from some one else, as they do a common cold. If they are susceptible to cold sores they will tend to get them for the rest of their lives irrespective of any contact with other sufferers. The sores will appear in response to changes in the condition of the human being that gets them.

Yet, in spite of this, the fluid from these sores is charged with a virus that is apparently responsible for the disease. It can pass on its infection to rabbits, but rarely to other adults.

This strange behaviour of the *herpes simplex* virus was heightened by the discovery that people susceptible to cold sores were carrying antibodies in the blood which were effective against the *herpes simplex* virus! And people who did not suffer from cold sores did not have any antibodies of this sort at all!

Before World War II the paradox of *herpes simplex* stimulated a great deal of research. Much of this has been carried out in Australia, where virus research is under the able leadership of Professor Sir F. M. Burnet, at the University of Melbourne.

Herpes simplex virus is a particularly co-operative organism which can be studied with comparative ease. It is not a dangerous virus, so that it can be handled with impunity in the laboratory. There is no shortage of the virus, which is always present in the saliva of people who suffer from cold sores.

Also the *herpes simplex* virus can be cultivated easily in the laboratory. It will grow on the cornea of a rabbit's eye and on living membranes of the hen's egg.

These simple techniques of cultivating *herpes simplex* have enabled scientists to detect either the virus or its antibodies in human hosts. The virus itself can be isolated and grown inside the egg; antibodies can be found in blood by mixing the serum with samples of virus. If the virus is destroyed the serum must contain *herpes simplex* antibodies.

Many adults have now been tested in this way; it has been established beyond all doubt that people who tend to get cold sores are carrying antibodies in their blood. People who never get a cold sore under any circumstances do not carry antibodies against the *herpes simplex* virus. This situation seems to be a permanent one in adults. Those who carry antibodies against *herpes simplex* will always have them; those who do not carry them will never have them, nor will they be infected with the virus during adult life.

The pattern of infection by *herpes simplex* virus is laid down during childhood. During the first few months of its life, a baby is carrying antibodies against *herpes simplex* virus in its blood. These antibodies have been given to the baby by its mother.

After a few months the antibodies disappear, and by the time the child reaches its first birthday it is no longer protected from infection by the virus.

Herpes simplex is extremely infectious, and the virus makes it way into the body through tiny cuts or abrasions on the lips and mouth. Young babies, always chewing and gnawing at anything they find, are rarely without slight wounds of this sort. So the *herpes simplex* virus finds its way into the body.

This first infection may cause a crop of sores, or may pass unnoticed. In either case the virus will have stimulated production of antibodies in the child's blood, and the infection is overcome. These antibodies will remain for life.

So far the infection and reaction have followed a typical course. But now the *herpes simplex* virus shows unusual traits. It is banished from the bloodstream by the antibodies; but instead of giving up its hold on the body, it settles down inside the deep-lying cells of the skin. Here it multiplies at a rate which is just sufficient to maintain its continued existence. As the skin-cells divide they carry a ration of virus inside them. But the virus does not embarrass the cells by multiplying too fast. It adjusts its rate to coincide with that of the cells themselves.

When children are infected in this way during the first few years of life they retain a colony of *herpes simplex* for the rest of their lives. So long as nothing goes wrong to upset the balance between virus and cells the virus is content to remain quietly at work keeping itself alive. It cannot spread to other parts of the body, as the antibodies in the blood would destroy it. But so long as it remains inside the living cell the virus in its turn is safe. Antibodies from the blood cannot penetrate inside the cell.

When something happens to upset this balance between the virus and the cell the *herpes simplex* viruses may start to multiply too quickly. The cells are damaged and destroyed and virus escapes into the surrounding tissues. But not for long. The antibodies in the blood are waiting for it, and the virus cannot extend its activities very far before being overcome. Soon it has retreated inside the cells again and is settling to its normal, humdrum pattern of life.

This is what happens when we get a crop of cold sores. For one reason or another something upsets the balance of activity in the body. Perhaps the body temperature is affected by too much heat or cold outside; perhaps some change in our metabolism is caused by emotional upset or by an unusual diet. Whatever it may be, the virus multiplication gets out of hand and the virus begins to destroy the cells in which it lives. We get an area of irritation set up which develops into a cold sore.

For some reason which we cannot yet understand infection by the virus of *herpes simplex* takes place only during early childhood. After the age of about five years a child is no longer susceptible to infection by the virus. At this age fate has decided whether it is to go through life with or without recurrent cold sores. If it has not been infected by that time it most likely never will be. And it will have no antibodies in its blood.

Experiments carried out by Professor Sir F. M. Burnet and his colleagues in Australia have established an interesting relationship between the incidence of *herpes simplex* and the general economic status of a community. Before the war a check was made of the *herpes* antibody-level in samples of blood from patients at a public hospital. Nearly every patient, young and old alike, had *herpes simplex* antibodies in the blood, showing that they had been infected with the virus.

Another check was made among the medical students and doctors in the hospital. This time only 37 per cent. showed infection by the *herpes simplex* virus.

The difference between these two groups was apparently due to the difference in their economic circumstances. On the whole the public hospital patients were from families less well-off than those of the medical students. During childhood the possibility of infection by *herpes simplex* decreases as the standards of housing and living conditions improve. Families are less crowded together and there is less likelihood of a child picking up infection from its brothers and sisters or its parents.

A similar survey was carried out after the war, when blood samples were taken from children attending private schools and from children in a hospital. This time there was a smaller difference between the two groups. The private school children from well-to-do homes again showed rather more than one in three infected with *herpes* virus. But the incidence among the hospital children was only about 55 per cent., compared with more than 90 per cent. among hospital patients before the war.

This fall in *herpes* infection in children from less well-off families is believed to be due to improvements in the standards of hygiene which have taken place in recent years. Parents are becoming more careful in their treatment of young children. Feeding equipment is now washed and sterilized, and there is a growing awareness of the need to protect young children from infection. So the *herpes simplex* virus cannot reach the child as easily as it used to. And more children are able to reach the age at which they are no longer susceptible to infection.

The *herpes simplex* virus is an excellent example of a parasite that has come to terms with its environment. All viruses are inevitably parasites—they can live only inside an appropriate living cell and therefore have no independent existence of their own.

In many ways parasitic existence has much to recommend it. Much of the work of living is delegated to some one else. But it has its drawbacks too. A parasite that destroys its host is endangering its own existence at the same time. A much more satisfactory arrangement is one that allows both parties to work in reasonable harmony together.

This is what the *herpes simplex* virus has done. It has learned to live and let live. Quietly and unobtrusively it multiplies inside the deep skin cells of its chosen home, content to remain in the background so long as the tenor of its life is undisturbed. Like most of us, it combines its liking for serenity with a degree of opportunism. If its host shows signs of weakness the virus will become obstreperous and burst from the cells in which it makes its home. But its exuberance is short lived; soon it is back in the safety of its cell again.

The problem of maintaining this parasitic existence of the *herpes* virus has been solved with admirable efficiency. A mother carrying *herpes* virus will pass on antibodies to the baby from her blood. But the antibodies fade away in a matter of months, so that the child is open to infection by virus from its mother's mouth.

Once infected, it will carry the virus for the rest of its days, passing it on in due course to its own offspring.

This happy arrangement has been arrived at only after thousands of years of association between the *herpes* virus and man. It is a masterpiece of companionable evolution, and represents a high point in virus progress. In all probability, other viruses will learn to emulate *herpes simplex*; we may find ourselves living amicably in permanent association with the viruses of polio or influenza.

9

Viruses and Animals

VIRUS diseases bring an immense burden of suffering through their direct attacks on man. But the virus is not content with that. It attacks our domestic animals as well, causing incalculable economic losses and striking at our precious food supplies.

As long ago as 1900 foot-and-mouth disease was recognized as being caused by a 'filterable germ'—a virus. In spite of everything we have learned about the virus in the last half-century, 'foot-and-mouth' remains one of the most dreaded of all animal diseases. It costs British agriculture nearly a quarter of a million pounds a year in slaughtered animals.

Foot-and-mouth disease affects not only cattle but pigs, sheep, goats, and other cloven-footed animals as well. Horses do not catch foot-and-mouth disease, but human beings have been known to be infected by the virus.

The blisters and sores that develop on the mouths and hooves of infected animals are painful and may take some weeks to heal. Foot-and-mouth disease is not often fatal; the animal will usually recover. But its vitality is seriously affected, and the milk yield of cows is severely reduced and may stop altogether. Cattle and pigs often lose as much as half their normal weight.

'Foot-and-mouth' is probably the most infectious of all animal diseases. Epidemics will sweep across a continent with astonishing speed. In many countries foot-and-mouth disease has established a permanent association with the animals it attacks, like influenza in human beings. Every now and again it flares up, causing great economic loss.

In Britain a policy of ruthless slaughter of all infected animals has kept the disease in check. As soon as foot-and-mouth disease is confirmed the animals are destroyed and the carcases burned. Movement of other animals in the vicinity is restricted and every precaution is taken to prevent spreading of the virus in other ways.

The virus of 'foot-and-mouth' is spread by direct contact between one animal and another, through droplets in the breath. It is remarkably infective and can also be carried indirectly in many ways. The bedding and drinking water of infected animals will pass on virus to other animals. Virus may also be taken from one farm to another on the boots and clothing of farm workers.

Although it is known that 'foot-and-mouth' virus can be spread about so easily in this way, it is often impossible to say how the virus reaches a district in which the disease first appears. 'Foot-and-mouth' will strike suddenly at cattle in an isolated farm; the nearest known source of infection may be hundreds of miles away.

One explanation of these outbreaks is that virus is carried to the farm on the feet of birds. Starlings or seagulls, for example, could bring 'foot-and-mouth' virus from infected areas in Europe, contaminating the drinking water or fodder of animals in British farms.

Small animals may also help to carry the virus from place to place. Rabbits and rats will act as hosts for 'foot-and-mouth' virus. Hedgehogs are known to suffer from the disease and will pass it on from one cow to another.

Many of the outbreaks in Britain in recent years have been traced to virus brought into the country in frozen meat. Viruses are not destroyed by freezing, and 'foot-and-mouth' outbreaks among pigs are often caused by virus in swill containing imported meat.

It has been suggested also that the virus of foot-and-mouth disease may have established permanent residence

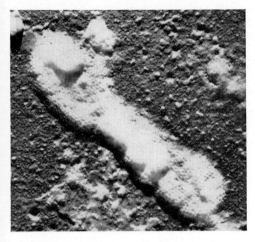

VIRUS GROWTH
IN BACILLI

This electron micrograph shows a pair of partly divided colon bacilli, attacked by T3 bacteriophages. The many new virus particles produced were packed in orderly fashion, leaving this imprint over the fibrous remains of the bacilli.

Photo Dr R. W. G. Wyckoff

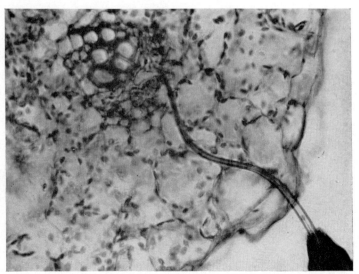

Photo Rothamsted Experimental Station, Harpenden

APHID CARRIER

Many plant viruses are transmitted by aphides. This photograph shows an aphid's feeding tube—which if infected, may leave behind a dose of virus—taking food-liquor from the vein of a sugar-beet leaf.

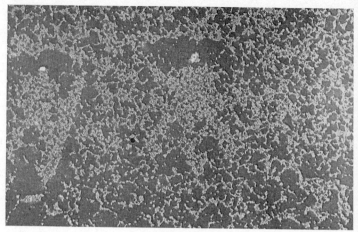

Photo Dr K. M. Smith, Agricultural Research Council

VIRUS SHAPES

Small and spherical, the plant virus Turnip Yellow Mosaic,
(×14,500.)

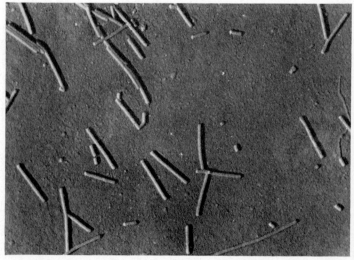

Photo Rothamsted Experimental Station, Harpenden

Rods of tobacco mosaic virus photographed through the electron
microscope.

in cattle, just as *herpes simplex* virus has in man. Under suitable conditions the virus flares up into sudden activity, causing the sores and blisters that are characteristic of the disease.

Vaccines are now being made and are widely used against foot-and-mouth disease in many continental countries. The job of vaccination is made more difficult by the existence of at least three strains of 'foot-and-mouth' virus. Infection of an animal by one strain of virus produces antibodies which protect it against future attacks by this strain, but not against either of the other two.

For many years vaccine needed for 'foot-and-mouth' has been made by injecting virus into the tongues of living cattle. Soon the virus has multiplied and typical 'foot-and-mouth' blisters appear on the tongue. The animal is killed and the virus collected and used for making vaccine.

This method has been used on a large scale in many countries, and it undoubtedly provides an effective vaccine for protecting animals from foot-and-mouth disease. But it is expensive.

Experiments carried out by Dr H. S. Frenkel, of the State Veterinary Research Laboratories in Amsterdam, have led to a new technique which is in many ways an improvement on the older one. Dr Frenkel showed that it is possible to cultivate 'foot-and-mouth' virus on tissue removed from the tongues of recently slaughtered cattle. The tissue can be kept alive for several days by keeping it cool, and virus will grow on the tissue when it is warmed just as it does in the living animal itself.

This new method of cultivating 'foot-and-mouth' virus, by avoiding the use of living animals, has put vaccination on a new economic footing. Vaccine can now be made on a scale that provides for immense vaccination schemes on a country-wide basis.

In Britain, where 'foot-and-mouth' has not established itself as it has in other countries, the slaughter of infected animals is still upheld as being the better policy.

Controversy has raged for many years over the merits and demerits of one control policy as compared with the other. From the point of view of the farmer who may have spent a lifetime building up a pedigree herd the destruction of his infected cattle is a major tragedy. He is compensated by the Government for his loss. But monetary compensation cannot make up for all the toil and care that he has put into the development of his herd. It is only natural that the farmer asks, "Why couldn't this be avoided by vaccinating the cattle to protect them from infection?"

The answer lies in the cost to the country as a whole. Slaughter appears to be an outrageous and extravagant method of dealing with foot-and-mouth disease when seen from an individual standpoint. But viewed from afar, it is much less costly than vaccination would be.

In 1951–52 an epidemic of foot-and-mouth disease swept over Europe. Starting in Germany in the summer of 1951, it reached Britain by early 1952, after travelling through Denmark, Holland, Belgium, Luxemburg, and France.

By mid-summer 1952 more than 250 outbreaks had occurred in Britain, starting from the eastern counties and reaching as far north as Aberdeen in Scotland. By June 1952 more than 28,000 animals had been slaughtered, including 14,326 cattle, 7759 sheep, 6401 pigs, and 20 goats. In May a standstill order prohibited the movement of animals throughout the country south of the Caledonian Canal in order to prevent the disease from spreading.

Rigid control measures of this sort, combined with the slaughter of infected animals, have kept foot-and-mouth disease from establishing itself permanently in Britain. The cost of slaughter over the ten years 1941–51 was about £220,000 a year; this was the amount of money paid out in compensation to farmers for animals which had to be destroyed.

This is a lot of money. But it compares very favourably with the damage done in countries where foot-and-mouth disease has become established. In Germany, for example,

the cost of a single epidemic in 1937–38 was estimated at
£83 million.

'Foot-and-mouth' vaccine is expensive to produce, but
the cost of administering it is even greater. To provide
adequate protection vaccine must be given twice a year to
the entire population of cloven-hooved animals. This is an
undertaking comparable in scope with the mass inoculation of children against polio.

The choice between slaughter and vaccination depends
very largely on prevailing conditions. In Britain we can
use slaughter effectively, as infection has not become
general and widespread. The same situation applies in
Ireland, Scandinavian countries, the United States,
Canada, and South Africa.

But in Germany foot-and-mouth disease is so common
that it would not be possible to destroy all infected
animals. Vaccination must therefore be used.

One of the disadvantages of the slaughter policy is that
it leaves the cloven-hooved animals of a country wide open
to attack. British cattle are in the same position with regard
to foot-and-mouth disease as the inhabitants of St Helena
were to polio before the epidemic struck them.

British cattle do not acquire any natural protection by
surviving an attack of foot-and-mouth disease. There are
no appropriate antibodies in the blood. And the cattle are
not stimulated to produce them by the injection of a vaccine. When a virus does reach Britain it has a free hand.

Countries with a slaughter policy are in this respect for
ever living on their nerves. One Congressman during the
1952 foot-and-mouth epidemic described the situation of
the United States farmers in the following words: "We're
sitting on a haystack with a prairie fire burning all around
us. A single shipment of infected material, a traveller who
had visited an infected farm, could start a conflagration
that might send our livestock industry and our meat and
milk supply up in smoke."

As the virus spread like wildfire over European countries

during 1952 only Australia and New Zealand, as well as the United States, managed to escape. Canada had its first outbreak of foot-and-mouth disease for eighty years; the virus was brought on the clothes of a German immigrant who had worked on an infected farm.

This outbreak, only sixty miles from the United States border, brought home to Americans the danger of the 'foot-and-mouth' situation. The slaughter policy had stifled five outbreaks of the disease in the United States since 1900. But it had also stifled research which could provide a stand-by protection against the threat of an overwhelming, nation-wide epidemic. There were at that time no facilities in the United States for studying foot-and-mouth disease; an ancient ruling of the Department of Agriculture had prevented any research being carried out. The risk of accidental infection was regarded as being too great.

Meanwhile the danger of the situation had been made apparent by experiences in Mexico. Since World War II Mexican farmers have been struggling against a catastrophic outbreak of foot-and-mouth disease that destroyed a million cattle in a year or two. The United States Government spent 120 million dollars in helping Mexico to overcome the disease that was raging just across the United States border.

This Mexican outbreak was an example of an attack too widespread and overwhelming to be stopped by slaughter. But with the help of mass vaccination it was eventually brought under control.

As the movement of livestock becomes more rapid and extensive the danger of a sudden, overwhelming outbreak of foot-and-mouth disease becomes ever greater. There is a growing realization that the policy of slaughter is essentially a stop-gap one. And vaccine research is going ahead in 'slaughter' countries despite the difficulties and cost.

Even in the hyper-sensitive U.S.A. a virus laboratory has been built at Plum Island, in Long Island Sound. Here scientists will search for a way of protecting the country's livestock from the growing threat of foot-and-mouth disease.

In Britain control of outbreaks by slaughter is much simpler than in the United States. Livestock is not transported over such immense distances, and counter-measures can be taken promptly and effectively to prevent the spread of virus. It seems likely that slaughter will remain the most economic policy for many years to come.

In due course the ever-widening use of vaccine may lead to an attempt to stamp out foot-and-mouth disease throughout the world. Britain will then, no doubt, fall into line with other countries and take part in mass control by vaccination.

In 1879 there was an outbreak of an unusual disease in Switzerland. The source of the infection was a strange one —an ailing parrot. Since then there have been epidemics of this ' parrot disease,' or psittacosis, from time to time, and many people have died of it.

Psittacosis is now recognized as a virus disease that affects parrots, budgerigars, and other birds. The virus can be grown in mice and eggs. It will infect human beings, causing a pneumonia-like disease that may be fatal.

For many years parrots took all the blame for epidemics of psittacosis. It was believed that the birds brought disease germs with them from their South American homes. In 1930 serious outbreaks of psittacosis occurred in Europe and the United States, caused by parrots that had been imported from Argentina. Scientists began to take the disease more seriously, and efforts were made to find the germ that was responsible. It was identified as a virus.

In an effort to get rid of psittacosis the United States authorities banned the import of parrots from South America. But still the disease kept breaking out, and search was made for some other ' carrier' of the virus. This time the culprit was the budgerigar.

These birds had been growing in popularity since the end of the nineteenth century. A large budgerigar-breeding industry had been built up in California, supplying people all over the United States with their pets. But a check-up showed that many of the Californian birds were infected with a psittacosis virus. And they were able to pass on the infection to man.

Birds bred in captivity are attacked by psittacosis when they are very young; they pick up the virus from infected droppings of their parents. Many birds die of the disease, but those that recover may continue to carry the virus. They can pass on infection in due course to their young in the nest.

This investigation of psittacosis cleared up some of the mysteries of the disease and showed what steps could be taken to prevent outbreaks in human beings. But it did not explain where the psittacosis virus had come from in the first place. So the researches were continued.

A shipment of birds was sent to California direct from the South Australian bushland where they had been caught. The budgerigars were examined before they came into contact with any cage birds. And many of them had psittacosis.

In 1935 Professor Sir F. M. Burnet extended the psittacosis research by examining hundreds of wild birds in Australia. Again, many of the adults were carrying psittacosis virus, although they were apparently quite healthy.

Psittacosis seems to be a 'natural' disease of birds of the parrot family. Infection is passed on from adult to young birds in the nest. If the bird recovers it may remain quite healthy even though it can pass on virus at a later stage.

When birds are kept under poor conditions they may succumb to a 'flare-up' of the disease. Sick birds can then distribute virus far and wide and may pass on infection to human beings.

During the 1930's scientists found that other birds were infected by psittacosis too. Inhabitants of the Faroe Islands suffered from recurrent epidemics of pneumonia which occurred particularly among women plucking young fulmar petrels. The 'pneumonia' was found to be psittacosis; virus was being distributed from the feathers of young infected birds.

Viruses of the psittacosis type are now known to infect many different birds; turkeys, chickens, pigeons, ducks, and pheasants have all been identified as sources of human psittacosis in the past.

In 1954 there were several outbreaks of psittacosis among workers in turkey-processing plants in Texas. The disease was much more severe than that which is caused by parrots or budgerigars. But treatment with antibiotic drugs prevented complications that caused many psittacosis deaths in the past. None of the cases of turkey psittacosis proved fatal.

By 1955 a way had been found of eliminating psittacosis from the pet birds that do so much to spread the disease around. Dr K. F. Meyer, of the University of California, discovered that birds could be cleared of psittacosis by injecting them with aureomycin or achromycin. The psittacosis virus is now known to be one of the few viruses that are sensitive to antibiotics and other drugs. The virus is a large one, and in many ways resembles a bacterium.

In foot-and-mouth disease and psittacosis we have two animal virus diseases of real relevance to human wellbeing. One attacks us by destroying animals that provide us with our food; the other attacks us directly by infecting us with disease.

There is another disease of animals that has been content to make its attack on man's friend, the dog. This is the virus disease, distemper, which had things very much its own way until a few years ago. Dogs infected by distemper had only a fifty-fifty chance of complete recovery. As in the case of human influenza, much of the damage was done by bacteria that attacked the weakened animal.

Distemper is no longer a serious disease. Vaccines have been made by cultivating virus, and these provide effective protection.

In 1954 a new and unusually interesting method of checking the distemper virus was claimed by United States scientists. Dogs actually suffering from an attack of distemper were cured by giving them a drug containing a dose of the anti-anæmia vitamin B-12 and the anti-arthritis pituitary gland hormone ACTH.

Nobody yet knows how this combination of substances is able to arrest the spread of distemper virus. The importance of the discovery is very much greater than its immediate applications would indicate. It is an example of a successful approach to virus control by influencing the metabolism of the virus as it multiplies in the cell. This is a technique that may enable us to make a direct, 'chemical' attack on viruses that are causing disease in the human body.

Although the distemper virus is extremely virulent and infectious, it does not carry any direct threat to man. Distemper is a disease that concentrates on dogs. But there is another virus infection of dogs that has its counterpart in man. This is the dreaded disease of hydrophobia, or rabies.

Rabies is a terrible disease; the spasms and convulsions of a rabies victim have been described as the most agonizing form of human suffering that can be imagined. Small wonder, then, that the fear of rabies can strike terror into people who are in danger of being infected by it.

Like distemper, rabies is primarily a disease of the dog. It is caused by a virus that is passed from one dog to another through the wound caused by a bite. The virus travels up the nerves to the spinal cord and brain, and makes its way to the salivary glands. When the dog bites some of the infected saliva is left in the wound. The virus enters the torn nerve fibres and the cycle of development continues.

The early symptoms of rabies usually appear a few weeks after the animal has been bitten. Often the dog will become indifferent to other dogs, or to people it knows. It has a bewildered appearance and tends to lick anything cold, such as stones or metal.

This is a dangerous period in the onset of rabies. There are none of the 'mad-dog' symptoms to act as a warning, yet the dog can pass on the rabies virus from its saliva.

As the disease runs its course the rabid dog becomes excited and its bark is hoarse. It wanders from its home, snapping at any living thing it meets. Then, after the illness has lasted for about a week, the dog falls exhausted in a ditch. Paralysis overtakes it, and it passes into a coma that ends in death.

The rabies virus can make its home in many warm-blooded animals. Rabies has been identified in foxes and wolves, skunks, weasels and stoats, badgers, jackals, hyenas, and grey squirrels. Many domestic animals can be infected by the bite of a rabid dog; cows, horses, pigs, sheep, cats, and goats are all susceptible to the disease.

In South America rabies is spread among cattle by the bite of the vampire bat. Even man has been given the disease in this way; the bats attack people as they sleep, feeding on their blood and passing on rabies virus in saliva they leave in the wound.

In Britain rabies was stamped out more than half a century ago. Regulations were enforced in 1897, and a policy of dog-muzzling and quarantine was carried through with immediate success. All dogs were muzzled in areas infected by rabies, and were kept muzzled for six months after the last case of rabies had occurred. Any dogs entering the country from abroad were kept in quarantine for six months. If they were carrying rabies they would show recognizable symptoms during that time.

Within two years of the introduction of these regulations rabies had disappeared from Britain, except for one district in Wales. Muzzling was no longer necessary, and it was relaxed. Wales suffered a flare-up in 1900, which was soon overcome. Since then rabies has been kept out of Britain, apart from an outbreak caused by a dog flown surreptitiously into the country after World War I.

Few countries are as fortunate as Britain in this respect. Rabies is still claiming hundreds of human victims every year. In tropical countries the sight of a rabid dog loping along, driving a crowd of terror-stricken people before it, is a familiar experience. Many people in India die from rabies after being bitten by infected jackals and wolves.

Although rabies is still causing deaths in this way, the disease was robbed of much of its power by Louis Pasteur in 1885. Pasteur found that the rabies virus in the spinal cord of an infected animal could be changed by appropriate treatment in the laboratory. By merely keeping the virus or by heating it its temperament could be modified. The longer it was kept, for example, the milder it became. The virus could be weakened in this way until it no longer caused the normal disease when deliberately injected.

On July 6, 1885, Pasteur took the courageous step of inoculating the first human being with his weakened virus; the patient was a child bitten by a badly infected dog. The experiment was successful, and by November 1888 the Institut Pasteur was founded to provide people with protection against rabies.

Pasteur's system of inoculation consisted of a series of injections with virus of gradually increasing virulence. The first inoculation was made with virus that had been weakened by keeping it for fourteen days. Then followed a series of daily inoculations using virus that had been kept for shorter and shorter periods. The final injection was made with powerful virus only three days old.

This system of inoculation develops the natural defences of the body in easy stages until they are able to overcome the dangerous 'wild' rabies virus.

In 1950 a vaccine was developed in the United States which protects the dog itself from infection by the rabies virus. The vaccine is made by growing rabies virus in hens' eggs. The virus changes as it multiplies in its new environment; injected into dogs it stimulates rabies antibodies without causing the disease. Protection lasts for several years.

Meanwhile research has continued to try and improve the inoculation technique used against human rabies. Pasteur's system has some disadvantages; a course of injections takes from two to three weeks, and there are sometimes dangerous side-effects.

In 1954 a serum became available which can be used in conjunction with the normal anti-rabies inoculations. Made from the blood of horses that have been immunized against rabies, the serum provides a direct and immediate supply of rabies antibodies. Injected into the blood of some one who has been bitten by a rabid dog, the serum speeds up the counter-attack by supplying ready-made antibodies.

This new anti-rabies serum does not replace the Pasteur inoculation system; it supplements it. When the victim has been bitten dangerously on the head or neck serum can provide instantaneous protection. Also it can shorten the inoculation treatment with anti-rabies vaccine, and minimize the danger of side-effects.

Now that these methods of protection against rabies are available, it should be possible to banish the disease from many countries in which it still exists. But the pool of infection in wild animals will prevent complete eradication of the disease. Like yellow fever, maintaining its existence in the blood of jungle monkeys, the virus of rabies will always be with us.

10

Insects suffer too

THE insect has a lot to answer for in its behaviour towards man. Insects eat our food and destroy our clothes. They burrow into the woodwork of our buildings. They bite and sting, and irritate us in innumerable ways. They spread disease, bringing misery and death to millions of people every year. But insects, in their turn, are plagued by their own particular brands of pests, including viruses.

Some insects, like the silkworm, are of direct economic importance to man. Anything that affects the well-being of these insects is of immediate interest to us. And for centuries we have been seeking to understand the diseases that destroy them.

In 1865 Louis Pasteur began his investigations into the diseases of silkworms which were to save the French silk industry from ruin. Pasteur showed that the diseases wiping out the silkworms were caused by tiny germs. And by rearing the worms in such a way as to avoid infection the spread of disease could be halted.

One of the diseases studied by Pasteur, flacherie, was in fact a virus disease. The germs that Pasteur saw in the bodies of diseased silkworms were microbes which had attacked insects already weakened by a virus infection.

Although it has long been realized that insects are attacked by viruses, comparatively little research has been done on this aspect of the virus story. But during the last ten years interest has been growing apace; insect viruses have extraordinary characteristics quite different from those of other animal viruses, and scientific curiosity has been roused.

Caterpillars seem to be particularly sensitive to virus attack. Infection often spreads with lightning speed, killing off the entire caterpillar population of a countryside. As the virus multiplies inside the caterpillar, the body of the insect becomes opaque and limp. The internal organs liquefy and the caterpillar disintegrates and dies.

The body of a caterpillar killed by virus disease is filled with liquid in which are floating innumerable tiny crystals. Often the outside of the caterpillar's skin is coated so thickly that it glistens like a layer of frost. The crystals are many-sided, and the diseases in which they appear are called polyhedral diseases.

Silkworms suffer from a polyhedral disease called jaundice, or ' grasserie,' and much of our knowledge of insect viruses has come from research on this disease.

At first it was believed that polyhedral crystals might be aggregates of the virus itself; millions of individual virus particles had packed alongside one another in the precise geometrical arrangement that is typical of a crystal. This seemed a reasonable explanation of the crystals, particularly when it was discovered that some plant viruses could be isolated in a crystalline form.

Experiments showed that polyhedral crystals were infective. As an insect died of polyhedral disease it left a legacy of crystals scattered about the plant on which it had been living. If then another susceptible caterpillar took in a ration of polyhedral crystal as it fed upon the plant it would become infected by the virus disease.

Polyhedral crystals are quite stable and can resist the effects of rain and sun. They will stay for several years, if necessary, on a plant or on the ground, waiting for an insect to come along and eat them. When an epidemic of polyhedral disease is at its height the crystals will lie like a layer of finely powdered snow. People walking through a forest in which caterpillars are dying of polyhedral disease may emerge with a film of polyhedral crystals on their clothes and skin.

In spite of the fact that polyhedral crystals can pass on a virus disease, they are not aggregates of the virus itself. Research has shown that they are much more complex bodies than was at first suspected. Virus particles make up only about one-twentieth of a polyhedral crystal. They are embedded in the centre of the material forming the crystal itself.

The bulk of a polyhedral crystal can be removed by dissolving it away, and the effects can be watched under a ' dark-field ' microscope.[1] As the crystalline material disappears a skin or membrane can be seen, similar to that covering a living cell or bacterium. Inside the membrane the solution of dissolved crystal material shows signs of continual movement; it is almost as though the liquid contains a mass of tiny particles that are being bumped about by the incessant movements of the agitated liquid molecules.

When the disintegrating polyhedral bodies are examined at even greater magnification, through an electron microscope, the particles set free inside the crystalline material can be recognized as virus particles. Photographs have been taken of these rod-like viruses embedded in tiny caves in the crystal substance.

This rod-shaped virus seems to be a characteristic of many polyhedral diseases of insects. Often the virus particles are bunched together like the sticks in a bundle of faggots.

Although these virus-charged crystals are known to pass on disease from one caterpillar to another, the process of infection is not as simple as it sounds. There is evidence that caterpillars carry a form of 'latent' virus in their bodies; like the *herpes simplex* virus in human beings, this caterpillar virus is content to remain quiescent until something happens to stimulate it into activity. Polyhedral

[1] See Chapter 15 of *We Live by the Sun*.

bodies may supply this stimulus and encourage the latent virus to multiply.

Caterpillars have in fact been bred through several generations under conditions in which they could not possibly be infected from outside with polyhedral disease. Then, suddenly, the disease has appeared as if from nowhere. Virus seems to be passed on from one generation to the next, remaining dormant until something happens that brings it back into active life.

The significance of the material surrounding the virus in a polyhedral crystal is still a mystery. It is not needed in the infective process. Silkworms can be given jaundice by infecting them with body-fluid that has been filtered to remove the polyhedral crystals. Free virus particles in the fluid are sufficient to cause disease.

Polyhedral diseases appear to infect only the larval stages in insects. In 1953 Dr F. T. Bird, of the Laboratory of Insect Pathology in Ontario, studied a deadly polyhedral disease of the European sawfly; he found that the virus was located only in large digestive cells in the intestine of the insect. As the sawfly larva changes into a prepupa—the stage between larva and adult insect—these large digestive cells disintegrate. They are replaced by cells that cannot be infected by the virus, and the insect at this stage is immune to infection by the virus. But as the development of the insect goes on digestive cells reappear, and the adult insect succumbs once more to the virus disease.

This insect, the European pine sawfly, has been the subject of an experiment in the deliberate use of virus to control an insect pest. The sawfly does immense damage to pine trees in European forests, hordes of larvæ stripping trees of their leaves. In 1939 the European sawfly appeared in Canada and settled down to make the most of the wonderful opportunities presented to it in Canadian forests. In ten years the insect had infested huge areas of Ontario and had become a serious pest.

In its European home the pine sawfly is subject to epidemics of polyhedral disease which help to keep the pest in check. In Canada no such disease had appeared during the sawfly's first ten years of residence, so it was decided that the disease should be imported and the insect infected artificially.

Stocks of polyhedral crystals were built up by breeding larvæ and infecting them with virus brought from insects living in Swedish forests. More than twenty gallons of liquid containing some 500,000 million polyhedral crystals were sprayed from aircraft on to infested forest; milk powder was added to the solution to make the crystals stick. In less than a month 94 per cent. of the sawflies had died of polyhedral disease.

One of the advantages of using viruses for pest-destruction lies in the amazing infectiveness of insect viruses. Mortality is high, and few insects will escape when an epidemic is thoroughly under way. Moreover, the polyhedral crystals used for spreading infection are not easily destroyed. They will lie in wait for the insect, their infective power undiminished, for several years.

Viruses are also specific in their action. We can use them to attack the insect we are fighting, without destroying useful insects in the process. This same selectiveness has made possible the use of myxomatosis virus for killing rabbits;[1] there is no danger of the virus harming our domestic animals.

These polyhedral diseases are probably the most extensive of all insect virus diseases, but there are other types as well. Many larvæ are attacked by viruses that form little granules inside the infected cells. There are no polyhedral crystals to act as containers for a group of virus particles; instead, each capsule carries a single virus particle inside it.

Polyhedral diseases are suffered exclusively by the insect world. The polyhedral bodies formed by viruses in caterpillars do not pass on disease to plants or higher animals

[1] See Chapter 6 of *The Fight for Food.*

or man. Like most viruses, those of insects are selective in their attack; they concentrate on one species of living thing to the exclusion of all others.

But not all viruses are so particular. As we have seen, yellow fever infects the monkey as well as man; the influenza virus will invade a ferret, and chimpanzees can catch a common cold.

So, in the insect world, we find that there are occasional exceptions to the general rule. The louse, for example, will die of a disease caused by the typhus virus it has picked up from its feed of human blood.

The louse enjoys the dirt and overcrowding that are inseparable from calamities such as floods and earthquakes, or the chaos caused by war. This tiny creature, with its hook-like feet, will cling in the hair or clothing of its human host, leaving the warmth and comfort of its home only to enjoy another feed of blood.

The louse is sensitive to the temperature of its surroundings; it likes the warmth of the human body, but dislikes any variation of even a degree or two from body temperature.

If the louse is feeding on a person suffering from typhus supplies of virus are taken in with the blood. The insect itself is infected by the virus and in a fortnight it is dead.

In the meantime the fever-heat of its human host will have made things uncomfortable for the louse. If other human beings are near it will escape from the over-heated clothes and settle down in any alternative accommodation it can find. As the virus multiplies inside the insect's body fæces infected with virus are left by the louse on the surface of its new host's skin. As the dying insect feeds it irritates its host, who scratches vigorously. Virus finds its way from the louse droppings into the broken skin, and the new host develops typhus.

During World War I epidemics of louse-borne typhus broke out wherever men were crowding together in the filth of trenches and shell-torn buildings. Lice were the

constant companions of soldiers on both sides of the lines.
There was some slight satisfaction to be gained from the
knowledge that the insects died from the effects of typhus
as well.

Inside the body of the typhus-infected louse virus multiplies in the walls of the insect's digestive system. As the
virus multiplies the cells are filled with new virus particles;
these are released into the insect's ' stomach' as the cells
burst. The louse dies of starvation caused by the disruption
of its digestive processes.

During World War I a related disease appeared which
was given the name trench fever. Like typhus, this was a
virus disease spread by the louse. But this time the virus
multiplied without damaging the cells of the insect's digestive system. The louse did not suffer from trench fever as
it did from typhus.

In this respect trench fever is comparable with other
insect-borne virus diseases such as yellow fever. The virus
is carried from man to man by the insect, which does not
itself suffer any ill-effects.

This immunity of the insect does not mean that its part
in spreading the virus disease is entirely a mechanical one.
The mosquito absorbs yellow fever virus as it sucks its
victim's blood. But for nearly a fortnight the insect is
unable to transmit the virus to another human being.
During this time the virus makes its way through the walls
of the mosquito's digestive cavity and into the blood. From
the blood it passes into the salivary glands and can be
injected into its next victim in the saliva that is left in the
tiny wound.

During its progress through the mosquito's body the
yellow fever virus multiplies. Yet the invasion of the mosquito by these highly active viruses does not appear to
inconvenience the insect in any significant way. The
material needed for constructing the new virus particles
must come from some of the tissues in the mosquito's
body. But the insect can apparently withstand the loss.

The part played by insects in the spread of animal disease is serious enough. But insects really come into their own in the plant world; they carry viruses in great variety from one plant to another.

Insects feed on every species of plant and on almost every part of every plant. Unlike man and the other animals, which can take avoiding action or discourage the attacking insect with a swishing tail or the flat of the hand, plants can do little to fight back. Insects can feed at leisure on the juicy tissues of the plant. And they do so in their overwhelming hordes.

As we shall see in Chapter 12, plants suffer even more than animals from virus diseases. Responsibility for maintaining the widespread distribution of these diseases lies largely with the insect.

Most plant-feeding insects are equipped with a tube that can be plunged into the sap-carrying vessels of the plant. The juices are sucked up through the feeding-tube, and a droplet of saliva is left behind in the plant. This saliva may contain a supply of virus that has been picked up earlier from an infected plant.

Aphides, like the common greenfly, carry innumerable viruses from one plant to another. Millions of pounds' worth of potatoes are lost every year through aphid-borne virus disease; almost every other agricultural crop is attacked by virus diseases that are spread by sap-sucking insects. One aphid alone, the peach aphis, is known to distribute at least twenty different plant viruses. It lives in almost every part of the world; in Britain this aphid carries the virus of potato leaf-roll, which is widespread wherever the peach aphis is to be found.

Insects can be as choosy in their transmission of plant viruses as they are with animal viruses. Just as yellow fever can be spread only by particular species of mosquito, so can the virus of leaf-roll in potatoes be carried from plant to plant only by the aphid. Most of the work is done by the peach aphis.

This selectiveness of insects for plant viruses is carried to remarkable lengths. Some diseases, such as ' streaks ' in maize, are carried not only by one species of insect but only by certain strains of that particular species.

This virus disease is spread from one plant to another by sap-sucking insects called leafhoppers. Experiments have proved that some strains of the leafhopper can carry the virus of maize streak and others cannot. The insects are indistinguishable in every obvious respect.

When leafhoppers are allowed to feed on infected plants virus can be found subsequently in the blood of the ' transmitting ' insects but not in the blood of the ' non-transmitters.' There is virus in the digestive system of the latter. But for some reason or other it cannot pass through the walls of the insect's ' stomach ' to reach the blood. It cannot, therefore, reach the salivary glands from which it would pass into the wound made when the insect feeds.

If a tiny hole is made with a needle in the wall of the ' non-transmitting ' insect's digestive tract the leafhopper then turns into a ' transmitter.' Virus can leak through into the insect's blood and reach the salivary glands.

Although most of the insects feeding on plants are equipped with sap-sucking devices, there are others such as beetles and caterpillars that feed by biting the plant and chewing the tissues.

Some of these biting insects can pass on viruses from one plant to another, but others cannot. The turnip flea beetle, for example, can infect a turnip plant with yellow mosaic disease. Other biting insects, including weevils, grasshoppers, and earwigs, can all spread yellow mosaic virus in this way. But the cabbage-white caterpillar, which is also a leaf-eater, is apparently unable to distribute the virus.

In the case of the sap-sucking insects, virus is injected into plants with the saliva. Yet in these biting insects the species that can spread virus from plant to plant are those which do *not* have salivary glands.

To explain this strange anomaly it has been suggested that insects lacking salivary glands must regurgitate some of the contents of their foregut during the feeding process. This would help in digesting the leaf tissue. As they bring up their food these insects infect the leaf with the virus from previous meals. Caterpillars, which are equipped with salivary glands, have no need to regurgitate, and they do not infect the leaves on which they are feeding.

So far as is known, the transmission of plant viruses by insects is usually a mechanical process. The insect picks up virus from one plant and leaves it behind in another one, like mud being scattered about the kitchen from a gardener's boots.

But infection is not always as simple as this. Plant viruses, in certain cases, are able to multiply inside the insect's body, just as the virus of yellow fever multiplies inside the mosquito.

Proof that a plant virus can multiply inside an insect has come from experiments carried out on leafhoppers in the United States. Leafhoppers were allowed to feed for two days on asters infected with 'aster yellows,' a virus disease. Then they were transferred to rye plants which do not carry this virus disease. The insects were examined at intervals, some of them being ground up with salt solutions to provide an extract of the virus from their bodies. The extracts were injected into virus-free insects after being diluted with water as much as one thousandfold. The insects were then allowed to feed on virus-free asters to see if they would pass on the infection.

By measuring how much the extract from the original insects could be diluted and still pass on infection, scientists estimated the amount of virus in the leafhoppers' bodies.

They found that the amount of virus increased from day to day after the insect had finished its meal on the infected aster plants. There was more virus in its body after a fortnight on a diet of virus-free rye than there was a day or two after its meal of infected aster. The virus had apparently multiplied inside the insect's body.

Support for this belief that plant viruses can make their home in insect cells comes from the fact that some aphides retain their ability to pass on viruses throughout their lives. Leafhoppers infected with the virus of dwarf disease of rice can hand on supplies of virus to their young.

Research carried out by L. M. Black, at the Brooklyn Botanic Gardens, New York, has shown that a leafhopper infected with the club-leaf virus of clover can pass on its infection through twenty-one generations of its descendants. The insects were raised on lucerne plants, which are immune to club-leaf disease and do not carry the virus.

This experiment offered convincing proof that plant viruses can, indeed, multiply inside their insect carriers. After passing through twenty-one generations, with as many as 150 offspring per generation, the virus would have become so diluted if it had not multiplied that it could not possibly have enabled the insects to pass on infection.

Yet, in spite of this evidence that some plant viruses can multiply inside the insect, there are plenty of examples of the rapid disappearance of plant viruses from the insect's body. Many aphides appear to destroy plant viruses in a few hours, and need to be in contact with fresh infection if they are to pass on the disease. Their powerful digestive juices are too much for the virus, which is broken up into harmless food chemicals.

The relationship between an insect and the plant virus it transmits may be much more than just an incidental one. Dr J. S. Kennedy, of the Agricultural Research Council Unit at Cambridge University, has carried out experiments which show that the black aphid mother produces 40 per cent. more young aphides per ' litter ' when feeding on virus-infected sugar beets than she does on virus-free plants.

Similar experiments with leafhoppers feeding on celery have shown how important a plant virus may be to the well-being of the insect that transmits it. Feeding on celery plants free of 'yellows' virus, the leafhoppers died out in a few days; but on diseased plants the leafhoppers flourished and multiplied into a little insect colony.

By making itself indispensable to the transmitting insect the plant virus ensures that its carrier will not neglect it. So, in this ingenious way, the virus makes certain of its continued survival in the future.

In this field of virus research, as in so many others, the behaviour of viruses is still full of mystery, and much remains to be done. If, in fact, the plant virus can multiply inside the insect's body this tiny organism, the virus, is acting as a chemical bridge between the plant and animal worlds.

11

Big Germs have Little Germs

WHEREVER there is life there is a struggle for existence. Every living thing is threatened by some other living thing; life for one means death for the other. In this unending fight the virus attacks wherever it can find a living cell. Some viruses take on the complex organisms, including man, made up from millions of co-operating cells; others are content to tackle the simplest of all living creatures, the bacteria, which have no more than a single cell to call their own.

The viruses that attack bacteria have become the focus of much of our modern virus research. With the help of the electron microscope we can watch the encounters between individual virus particles and individual bacterial cells. We can study the behaviour of attacking viruses with a precision that is denied us when we have to deal with more complicated multicellular victims of the virus.

These bacterial viruses have achieved the distinction of being given a special name. The French bacteriologist Felix d'Herelle, who helped to discover bacterial viruses during World War I, called them bacteriophages. Nowadays we often use the less exacting name of ' phage.'

The discovery of these bacterial viruses, or phages, took place in Britain and France almost simultaneously. The approach was different in each case, but the conclusions reached were much the same. Professor F. W. Twort, in Britain, and Dr Felix d'Herelle, in France, announced to the world that bacteria responsible for so many human diseases were themselves attacked by even smaller microbes. These 'lesser germs of bigger germs' could not be seen through the optical microscope. They must be viruses.

In 1915 Professor F. W. Twort, of London University, was studying the food requirements of bacteria. Already he had shown that there was an essential substance—what we now know as vitamin K—which bacteria needed for proper growth. Twort's researches extended to a study of the viruses. And he was using the cheap and readily-available vaccinia (cowpox) virus used for smallpox inoculations.

At that time the lymph containing vaccinia virus was often contaminated with bacteria that could produce minor infections during vaccination. If lymph was spread on the surface of a jellified broth containing bacterial foods, and then incubated, the bacteria would multiply and form little colonies on the jelly. Each colony, containing perhaps millions of bacteria, could be seen with the naked eye.

The vaccinia virus in the lymph, in common with all viruses, did not grow on broth in this way. Viruses will multiply only inside an appropriate living cell.

Professor Twort made 'cultures' from his lymph. He found, as expected, that the bacteria in the lymph multiplied into visible colonies. Given time, these colonies would spread until the surface of the jellified broth was almost covered by a layer of bacteria.

But when he examined some of his cultures closely Twort found that there were sometimes clear spots where the bacteria had not multiplied. These clear spots tended to spread, growing into patches that eventually united until all the bacteria had disappeared. It looked just as though an epidemic of some sort of disease was spreading through the millions of bacteria on the surface of the broth.

Twort was astonished by this discovery, and continued with his experiments. He found that the bacterial ' disease '

was infectious. By touching a clear patch on a diseased
culture with a glass rod, and then touching a healthy bacterial culture with the rod Twort found that the healthy
bacteria became infected. Gradually the jelly on which
they grew would become transparent as the bacteria
died.

These experiments, in many respects, resembled those
which were to lead to the discovery of penicillin by Sir
Alexander Fleming in 1928. Fleming found, like Twort,
that flourishing colonies of bacteria could be destroyed.
But the antagonist in Fleming's experiment was easily
recognized; it was a mould which destroyed bacteria near
it by generating a lethal chemical. This chemical was what
we now know as penicillin.

Twort's bacterium-killing agent differed fundamentally
from the penicillin that was subsequently to cause such a
revolution in the medical world. The bacteria were being
destroyed, not by a chemical, but by a living infective
microbe. As it invaded a bacterial cell the microbe multiplied, releasing a family of new microbes that could spread
the disease to other bacteria.

Twort made extracts of the clear patches in cultures of
bacteria and filtered the extracts through bacterium filters.
The clear liquid contained no germs visible through the
optical microscope. Yet it retained its power of infecting
bacteria. The infective agent could only be a virus. So, by
1915, the world was astonished to learn that the germs
that cause so much of our human disease have their own
health-troubles too.

Meanwhile another bacteriologist had been making his
way towards this same discovery. Dr Felix d'Herelle, on
September 15, 1917, sent a note to the French Academy of
Science "on an invisible microbe, an antagonist of the
dysentery bacillus." He called the invisible microbe ' bacteriophage,' meaning ' eater of bacteria.'

D'Herelle's researches were part and parcel of his work
as a practical bacteriologist in the field of public health.

Before World War I d'Herelle was conducting an anti-locust campaign in Mexico; the insects were being destroyed by infecting them with a form of locust dysentery. From Mexico, d'Herelle moved to North Africa, bringing this technique of biological pest-control[1] to the struggle against locusts that had been going on there since Biblical times.

Locusts were infected by dusting cultures of the germs on to plants in the path of the swarm. Supplies of germ-cultures had to be organized on a big scale, and d'Herelle had plenty of opportunity of studying any peculiarities of germ growth. He found, as Twort had done, that clear patches would often appear on some of his culture tubes. He examined the patches under his microscope but could see nothing.

In March 1915 d'Herelle was in Tunisia, spreading epidemics of disease among locusts that were threatening the war-time harvests. At the Pasteur Institute in Tunis he was able to examine the clear patches in his bacterial cultures in some detail. He tried to infect locusts with the clear liquid made by filtering cultures carrying the clear spots. But without success; the virus—if virus it was—did not affect the locust itself.

Later in the summer of that year d'Herelle moved to Paris; dysentery had broken out in a squadron of cavalry, and he was given the job of investigating the disease. D'Herelle found in this work a wonderful opportunity of continuing his research into the intriguing mystery of the clear spots in bacterial cultures.

He isolated dysentery germs from the fæces of his human patients, and cultivated them in the traditional manner on jellified broth. As usual the germs multiplied and formed their visible colonies on the surface. And, as d'Herelle anticipated, some of the cultures were speckled with clear patches where the colonies of germs were being destroyed.

[1] See Chapter 2 of *The Fight for Food.*

D'Herelle set out to try and find some pattern of logic behind the appearance of these clear spots. He cultivated dysentery germs obtained at daily intervals from a patient; to each culture he added the clear liquid obtained by passing a fæces extract through a bacterial filter. For three days the dysentery germs grew into colonies as expected. But on the fourth day of the patient's illness the germs grew for a time and then 'wilted' and gradually disappeared. The jelly of the culture tube was left transparent and clear. Something in the clear filtered liquid from the patient's fæces was attacking the germs that had been isolated from the same source.

Excited by his discovery, d'Herelle ran from his laboratory to the hospital. As he had expected, the patient had turned the corner and was now on the way to recovery. The dysentery germs in his body were being overcome, as he supposed, by the invisible microbe that had suddenly appeared among them.

D'Herelle saw the immense significance of his discovery. If these invisible enemies of bacteria—these viruses—were responsible for the natural recovery of a victim of disease, could they not be used deliberately in the same way? Was it possible to treat disease by infecting with viruses the bacteria that caused it?

After publishing his first note about 'bacteriophages' in 1917 d'Herelle continued his researches in an effort to put his discoveries to practical use. At that time neither he nor Twort could prove that the bacteriophages existed by showing them through the microscope. More than twenty years had to pass before the electron microscope could remove all doubts by taking photographs of bacteriophages. Many scientists were reluctant to believe that the discoveries of Twort and d'Herelle were due to anything more than chemical destruction of bacteria. The idea of an invisible germ that infected a germ itself was too incredible to be true.

D'Herelle, however, went on to show that there were

many strains and species of bacteriophages. Some were specific in their action, attacking only a single species of bacterium; others were more versatile, invading and destroying a wide range of different bacteria. Some bacteriophages were sensitive creatures that lived for only a day or two; others were able to survive being sealed away in test tubes for years without losing the ability to infect their bacterial hosts.

Between the two World Wars d'Herelle and his supporters carried out an enormous amount of research on the bacteriophages. Much of it was concerned with the practical aspects of the use of these extraordinary viruses in the treatment of disease.

D'Herelle himself continued with his investigations on the bacteriophages that attack the germs of dysentery. He found that, at first, the viruses present in the fæces of a patient were active only against the familiar *B. coli* which is always present in the human intestine. For a few days, as the dysentery germ consolidated its attack, the position remained the same. Then suddenly the bacteriophages would begin to switch their attention from *B. coli* to the dysentery bacilli. As the attacking viruses overcame the disease germ the patient would show signs of getting better; thanks to the bacteriophages, d'Herelle believed, recovery would soon be on its way.

D'Herelle carried out an investigation on human cholera during the 1920's, intent upon extending his knowledge of the part that bacteriophages play in human disease. First in Indo-China and then in India he showed that the appearance of bacteriophages in the patient's fæces by the second day of the disease was a sign that the invading germs could be overcome. Only a massive attack by bacteriophages would ensure recovery; if none at all had appeared death was certain.

D'Herelle concluded that the appearance of bacteriophages was the sole reason for a patient's recovery from cholera. He switched his researches to bubonic plague, and claimed that the same pattern of infection and counter-infection could be traced for this disease.

One of the most remarkable of all d'Herelle's investigations was carried out on a disease of hens—fowl typhoid. This disease is highly infectious and lethal; it spreads with great speed through a flock of poultry. In his study of fowl typhoid d'Herelle found that the disease would often kill off every bird infected. Then suddenly a hen would recover, and bacteriophages active against the typhoid germ could be found in its droppings.

Once this had happened other hens would survive. Soon recovery had reached 'epidemic' proportions as the bacteriophages spread throughout the flock. The cure was as infectious as the disease itself.

In 1927 d'Herelle discovered that the same thing happened in the case of human cholera. During epidemics of cholera in India the disease would sweep through a community. Then, suddenly, a cholera victim would recover; bacteriophages active against the cholera germ would appear in his fæces. And an epidemic of cure would then take over from the disease as the viruses were spread from one person to another.

The next step to be taken was an obvious one. Could the bacteriophage be cultivated deliberately on colonies of bacteria and used in the treatment of disease? D'Herelle carried out an experiment on birds and claimed that he was able to stop an epidemic of fowl typhoid by putting supplies of bacteriophages in the birds' drinking water. Encouraged by this success, he went a step farther and found that bacteriophages could be used successfully for treating dysentery in children. The virus was given by mouth.

During the 1920's and 1930's these discoveries naturally stimulated a great deal of research; the claims made by d'Herelle opened up wonderful prospects in the control of infectious disease. Many attempts were made in Germany, Brazil, and the United States to repeat the work, but the results were disappointing. Bacteriophages did not live up to the reputation that they had so suddenly acquired. Hopes of using them effectively against disease began to fade.

The difficulties of making practical use of bacteriophages in this way stem from characteristics that we now recognize as typical of other viruses. The bacteriophages are fickle and will change the detailed make-up of their personalities easily and quickly. New strains appear which have their own individual tastes in the bacterial hosts that they prefer. Bacteriophages cultivated in a pedigree strain of a bacterium kept in the laboratory will not necessarily attack the strain of bacterium that is causing an epidemic of disease.

Even in the early experiments carried out in Britain it was noticed that there are always some bacteria that are not destroyed by a bacteriophage. Resistant bacteria could be seen here and there in the transparent patches where the majority of the germs were being destroyed.

These resistant germs can nullify our efforts to overcome bacteria in the body with the help of bacteriophages. They can multiply so fast that they soon replace the destroyed bacteria with a brand-new population of bacteriophage-resistant germs.

The real value of bacteriophages in coping with infectious diseases has yet to be resolved. Undoubtedly the claims that were made originally were unduly optimistic. Failure on the part of competent and conscientious scientists to duplicate many of the experimental results has led to a great deal of scepticism which is not easily overcome. Also the late 1930's saw the introduction of remarkably effective new drugs for tackling disease germs in the body. First came the sulpha-drugs; and then during World War II the antibiotics. It seemed, at one time, as though the danger from disease germs was on the point of being dispelled for good. Interest in bacteriophages waned.

But in some countries experiments have continued. Bacteriophages are still being used in India, Egypt, and Russia for fighting dysentery and plague. Good results have been claimed against cholera in India, where bacteriophages are put into wells of drinking water during epidemics.

Now that disease germs are becoming resistant to many of our modern wonder-drugs, it seems likely that research on the use of bacteriophages will increase. Meanwhile these little organisms have established themselves in a brand-new career in the world of academic science. They are providing us with an admirable tool for the study of viruses and their behaviour in the living cell.

The electron microscope has shown us that there is a great variety of bacteriophages. Some are so small that they are no larger than the viruses of polio or foot-and-mouth disease; others are almost big enough to be seen through the optical microscope.

Unlike so many of the viruses that attack the higher animals and plants, bacteriophages have a characteristic tadpole shape. They can be distinguished easily from other particles in a mixture; they can be located more precisely, for example, than a typical 'ball' of influenza virus.

Much of the research on bacteriophages has been carried out on seven different strains that attack the germ of *B. coli*. These bacteriophages are described as T1, T2, T3, T4, T5, T6, and T7. The odd-numbered viruses have spherical heads and thin, curly tails. The even-numbered bacteriophages are more square-headed, and all have short, stiff tails.

Like other viruses, the bacteriophages show no signs of independent life. Outside their host-cells they are dead. They will not absorb any food from their surroundings, nor do they need any oxygen to release energy from their body-substances. But in the presence of their bacterial hosts these little inanimate tadpoles are able to come to life. They move towards the bacteria, attracted by elec-

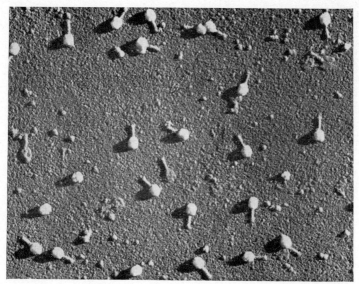

Photo Dr A. E. Vatter, Electron Microscope Laboratory, University of Illinois

BACTERIOPHAGES

These 'tadpole' viruses are T2 bacteriophages magnified 57,000
times.   The many-sided heads can be clearly seen.

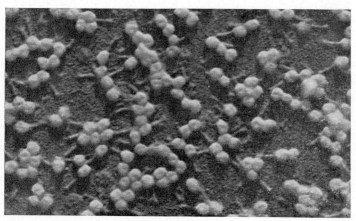

Photo Dr R. W. G. Wyckoff

Clusters of coli bacteriophages.   ($\times$30,000.)

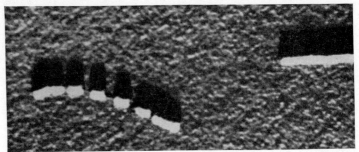

Photo Dr Paul Kaesberg, University of Wisconsin

TOBACCO MOSAIC VIRUS

(*Above*) Virus broken by freeze-drying. The nucleic acid core can be seen joining the broken fragments. (×150,000.)

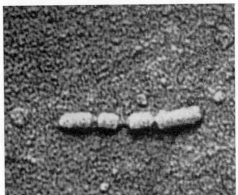

(*Left*) Virus particle from which sections of the outer protein shell have been removed. The thread of nucleic acid joining the remaining sections can be seen. (×150,000.)

(*Right*) Viruses undergoing disintegration. The nucleic acid threads left behind after removal of the protein coat can be seen.

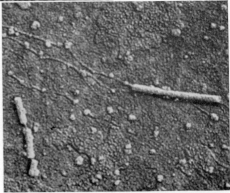

Photos Professor G. Schramm, Max-Planck Institute for Virus Research, Tübingen

trical forces. They do not propel themselves in any normal 'living' way; the tails of bacteriophages cannot wiggle like those of tadpoles.

When it has reached the bacterium towards which it is attracted the bacteriophage is able to penetrate the wall of the bacterial cell. In a few minutes the bacteriophage will have multiplied; the cell wall bursts and 100 or more new bacteriophage particles emerge. They are ready immediately to attack bacteria and multiply on their own account.

This rate of multiplication is so fast that a colony of bacteria growing on a culture-dish is soon overwhelmed and destroyed. The transparent culture medium that remains may contain as many as 2 million million bacteriophages to the cubic inch.

With the help of the electron microscope we can now watch what happens when a bacteriophage reaches the single-cell bacterium in which it hopes to multiply. First, the bacteriophage attaches itself to the cell-wall by its tail; the 'head' of the bacteriophage is not in contact with the cell.

As soon as this happens the normal work of the cell comes to a stop. The bacterium can no longer go on with its job of piling up the stores of cell material that will enable it to multiply by splitting into two daughter cells. Instead the little cell factory is taken over by the invading virus. The bacterium's fate is sealed. From now on its efforts will be directed towards self-destruction; its living substances will be used as raw material for the production of a batch of new bacteriophages.

At first the bacteriophage is held on to the bacterium wall by forces of electrical attraction, like iron being held by an electromagnet. Then the virus consolidates its hold, dissolving away the material of the cell-wall by chemical action. Through the hole that is formed the virus substance makes its way into the cell and begins to multiply.

The details of this penetration process have been studied intensively, particularly with the T2 bacteriophage attack-

ing *B.coli.* The bacteriophage itself is designed in the
form of a hollow capsule containing a supply of complex
chemicals similar to those that make up the nucleus of a
living cell. The shell of the bacteriophage is made of protein; it resembles the protein skin with which the human
body is surrounded.

The protein tail of the virus is hollow, forming a tiny
tube; the bulbous head contains the supply of nucleic acids
—complicated life-chemicals that are always present in
any living cell. The bacteriophage is, in fact, a tiny syringe,
with a protein bulb and tube and a charge of nucleic acid
packed into the bulbous head.

As it anchors its protein shell to the cell-wall of its victim
the bacteriophage is at first held only by the electrical
forces which have brought the two particles together. At
this stage the two can be separated again. But once the
bacteriophage has consolidated its hold on the cell nothing
can be done to save the bacterium.

As soon as the virus has penetrated the cell-wall the tiny
syringe empties its contents into the bacterium. The
nucleic acids are injected through the tubular tail of the
virus, and into the cell. The protein skeleton of the bacteriophage remains outside the bacterium; its work has
been done.

Inside the cell the nucleic acids injected by the virus
take part in a chemical mêlée. For several minutes the
work of self-reproduction and reassembly goes on. There
are no recognizable virus particles in the cell; the original
material has lost its identity in the general mix-up of
chemical reconstruction.

Then, after perhaps ten minutes, there are signs of some
order appearing from the chaos. New virus particles can
be seen inside the cell, forming a pattern against the remnants of the cell contents. In due course the cell-wall
bursts, and the new bacteriophages are set free, ready to
seek out host-cells of their own.

This extraordinary reproduction process takes place in a

world so small that it is beyond our human comprehension. The 'head' of a typical bacteriophage is only fifty-five millimicrons in diameter. Its tail is 225 millimicrons long.

In spite of the bacteriophage's resemblance to a tadpole, it shows no signs of life outside the living cell of its bacterial host. Like some other viruses, bacteriophages can be purified. They behave as normal chemicals, and can be analysed and studied as though they were crystals of a vitamin or a natural drug extracted from a plant.

This chemical approach to bacteriophages has given us a vantage point from which we can see something of the chemical behaviour of the living cell itself.

12

The Persecution of Plants

FOR more than half a century tobacco has been at the centre of much of our virus research. The tobacco plant suffers more than most living things from attacks by viruses. It is plagued, in particular, by a virus that causes the historic tobacco mosaic disease.

The leaves of a tobacco plant infected by mosaic disease are mottled with patches of yellow or pale green. This mosaic-like pattern was recognized as the symptom of a definite disease in 1885; seven years later Dmitrii Iwanowski carried out the experiments which were to show that it was caused by an invisible germ. A virus.

So tobacco made an early entry into the field of virus research. And it has remained ever since a convenient and co-operative medium for the study of plant viruses. In 1935 tobacco mosaic virus featured in another great step forward in virus research. The American scientist, Wendell Stanley, separated crystals of the virus from the sap of infected plants. This was the first time that a virus had been isolated and purified in a typically 'mineral' form; millions of individual particles of tobacco mosaic virus had aligned themselves into a precise geometrical pattern just as ordinary atoms do when they form the crystals of a chemical such as salt or sugar.

Since then much of our knowledge of plant viruses has come from a study of tobacco mosaic disease. The ease with which pure virus can be isolated has given us a useful starting point for fundamental virus research.

Viruses attack the plant world with an enthusiasm no less than that which they show towards animals. More than 150 different plant viruses have been recognized; many of them will infect a wide range of plants. Tobacco mosaic virus, for example, will cause a mosaic disease in tomatoes too; anemones are attacked by the virus that causes mosaic disease in cucumbers.

Most viruses are content to invade their plant hosts without destroying them completely. Survival of the virus depends upon survival of the plant in which it makes its home. The virus tends to debilitate its victim rather than to kill it.

As it multiplies inside the living cells of its host the virus leaves its mark upon the surface of the plant. Chlorophyll is destroyed, leaving etiolated patches, or concentric rings and spots that disfigure the leaves. Where chlorophyll has gone the leaf-cells can no longer absorb the sunlight and use it to power the food-manufacturing processes of the plant.

Some types of virus cause spectacular side-effects in the invaded plant. Little sub-leaves sprout beneath the true leaves; plants grow sideways rather than upward, and vice versa; distorted flowers with thick green petals are borne on the end of short, squat stalks. Occasionally a virus will run amok, causing serious wounds and cutting off the supply of food and water to essential tissues. A plant that is attacked too viciously in this way may wilt and die.

The economic effects of virus-attack on our agricultural crops are difficult to assess. But there is no doubt that viruses are responsible for immense food losses every year.[1] Potatoes, one of the vital food crops of the western world, are attacked by many virus diseases. Mosaic, leaf-roll, and potato virus X can, between them, reduce the crop by 50 per cent. In Britain alone we lose as many as 1 million tons of potatoes in a season through virus attack. The impregnation of our crop by viruses prevents us keeping seed

[1] See Chapter 4 of *The Fight for Food*.

potatoes from one year to the next; normally we bring 500,000 tons from Scotland every season.

Sugar beet is another crop that is attacked severely by viruses. Beet infected by mosaic and 'yellow' will often produce only half the normal yield of sugar. In the United States the depredations of the sugar beet viruses are so overwhelming that beet-growing has been abandoned altogether in some districts.

In other ways too plant viruses have been leaving their marks for as long as man can remember. An invading virus will often affect the flowers of a plant, sometimes distorting and stunting, occasionally adding a contribution towards the beauty of the flower as a whole.

The delicate tracery and markings that we call 'breaks' on tulips are caused by viruses. The petals are often streaked by feathery lines and patches of lighter colour, creating an effect so unusual that these virus-infected tulips were once sold as expensive and greatly-prized rarities.

Daniel Rabel, in paintings he made nearly 300 years ago, includes tulips with 'breaks.' The great Rembrandt saw beauty in flowers that we now know to be infected with virus disease.

For a long time scientists were puzzled by streaks that appeared in blood-red wallflowers; yellow patches and lines would pattern the petals in much the same way that they do in the tulip. It was found that these flowers too were being infected with virus disease. Aphides were responsible for spreading the virus from plant to plant, and virus was brought, in the first place, from cabbages and broccoli suffering from black ring spot. In wallflowers this ring spot virus appeared as streaks in the flower petals. It affects other flowers as well, including honesty and stocks.

Most viruses, once they find their way into a susceptible plant, will multiply and spread throughout the tissues of the plant. But a strange virus was discovered by research workers at Cambridge which does not behave in this way.

Tobacco plants growing in insect-proof glasshouses were found to have a virus in their roots. Yet the plants were healthy, and there was no sign at all of any virus in the stem or leaves.

Even more astounding was the fact that these tobacco plants could be infected artificially with their own virus! Some of the roots were ground up and the virus extracted; when the virus extract was rubbed gently into the leaves the plants became infected by a severe virus disease. They succumbed to virus that was already living harmlessly in their own roots.

This 'tobacco necrosis' virus is carried from one plant to another by soil water, and by the air. It is not transmitted by insects. Unless it penetrates into the upper part of the plant, for example through a leaf that rubs against the soil, it remains in the roots without having any noticeable effect on the health of the plant.

This soil-borne virus can only make its way into the tobacco plant roots through an open wound. Tobacco plants can be grown in a jar of water impregnated with virus, and the roots will remain virus-free. But in the soil the movement of roots past soil particles is for ever breaking off the delicate root-hairs. And virus can enter the plant through the tiny openings that are made.

The roots of the tobacco plant, by maintaining a virus infection in this way, are acting as ' carriers '—similar to infected people who can spread the viruses or germs of human disease without suffering ill-effects themselves. This example of one part of a plant acting as a virus carrier is an unusual one. But there are many plants that can maintain a supply of virus in normal distribution in their tissues without showing any obvious symptoms of disease.

The King Edward potato behaves in an extraordinary way towards the virus. This well-known variety of potato was used by R. N. Salaman during the 1920's in a series of grafting experiments. And to the astonishment of all concerned it transmitted a virus disease to the other varieties of potato on to which it was being grafted. The infection was a severe one.

The King Edward plants from which the grafts were being made were perfectly healthy and showed no signs of virus disease. Yet they never failed to pass on a virus infection to other plants.

This strange phenomenon was studied carefully, and it was found that all King Edward potatoes are carrying a virus in their tissues. The virus does not have any apparent effect on the plant; there are no symptoms of disease. The virus is not spread naturally from King Edwards to other potato plants; insects do not carry the infection, nor does artificial inoculation of King Edward sap into other potatoes have any effect. Only by grafting does the virus pass from the King Edward potato into other plants.

Normally a severe disease is caused when King Edward virus is passed to other plants in this way. But some varieties of potato can accept the virus without suffering any ill-effects. The virus multiplies inside them, as it does in the King Edward, but makes no external changes in the plant to show that it is there.

Nobody has yet explained how the King Edward virus got into this variety of potato in the first place. It has never been found naturally in any other variety of potato, nor in any other host-plant. Even if it had, there is no known method of passing on the infection except by grafting.

If the King Edward variety had been evolved from unusual parents in some out-of-the-way part of the world we could take refuge in our ignorance of the plants from which it came. But there is no indication that this variety of potato came from any particularly exotic parents; it was evolved by a gardener in Northumberland.

It may well be that this mysterious virus has more academic significance than we realize. Perhaps it is a normal part of the metabolism of the King Edward potato which becomes an infective virus only when it is stimulated by strange surroundings?

In common with all viruses, those which live in plants are highly infective. Once a few virus particles can find their way into a susceptible plant they will lose no time in multiplying and establishing themselves throughout the tissues.

But viruses are big particles compared with the tiny molecules of water, carbon dioxide, and oxygen that move to and fro so easily between the plant and the outside world. The virus particle can enter a plant only through a puncture or wound that breaks the surface layers of the leaf or stem.

Sometimes viruses can move from one plant to another when close-packed plants are blown against each other by the wind. Tiny wounds are opened in the leaves, which allow the virus particles to pass from one plant to the other.

As we have seen in Chapter 10, most of the mechanical work of transporting virus from plant to plant is done by insects. Millions of feeding-tubes are for ever plunging into the tissues of plants as insects search for the sap that provides them with their food. And by preventing insects from feeding on crop plants we can do much to stop the spread of virus diseases.

Unfortunately ordinary contact insecticides are often disappointing in their use against virus-carrying insects. They seldom act quickly enough to prevent an insect picking up a dose of virus and then transferring it to another plant. The introduction of systemic insecticides is speeding up the insect-killing process and will undoubtedly do much to give us an adequate control over many virus-spreading insects.

Systemic insecticides, which enter into the plant's tissues and circulate in its sap, deliver a dose of poison to the insect as it feeds. If the poison acts quickly it may kill the insect before it can make its way to another plant. Although the plant that kills the insect will prevent the creature passing on virus to another plant, it will not necessarily avoid infection itself. As the insect enjoys its last meal it will leave a dose of virus in the plant that is killing it.

Insecticides of this sort can therefore do a lot to stop insects spreading virus from one plant to another in a field. But they will not necessarily stop infection reaching plants from outside. If infected aphides are reaching a field in a steady stream from elsewhere they will be able to infect the plants on which they settle. One aphid can provide the virus necessary to infect a plant. And aphides commonly arrive in hordes containing millions at a time.

The critical effect of the time an insect takes to die has been shown in the case of viruses affecting potato crops. Most of the spread of leaf-roll virus in a British potato field is due to infection passed from one plant to another by 'local' aphides in the field. Few aphides arrive from distant areas of infection.

The virus of leaf-roll absorbed by an aphid as it feeds on an infected plant is not available immediately to infect another plant. For some hours after its feed the insect cannot pass on its infection. A systemic insecticide sprayed on to potatoes can therefore do a lot to stop the spread of leaf-roll virus through the field. An aphid feeding on an infected plant receives a dose of insecticide as well as virus. It may have time to feed on one or two other plants in the vicinity before the insecticide takes effect. But by the time the virus in the aphid could be passed to another plant, the insect is dead.

By contrast there is another virus that affects potatoes, called potato virus Y, which can be passed on almost immediately by an infected aphid. There is no 'incubation' period during which the aphid is non-infective. Unless an insecticide kills the aphid with sledge-hammer speed, it can do little to stop the spread of potato virus Y. If the insect lives for only a few minutes after taking in its dose of insecticide it still has time to spread potato virus Y to other plants near by.

Although insecticides are undoubtedly a useful weapon against plant viruses, they cannot help us to cure plants already infected with virus disease. And viruses are often established in crops, causing chronic diseases that are passed on from one ' generation ' to the next.

As a rule viruses are not transmitted from a parent plant to its offspring through the seed. This may be due to the inability of the virus to make its way into the embryo in an infected plant. In 1955 N. C. Crowley, of the Waite Agricultural Research Institute in Adelaide, Australia, showed that plant seeds contain chemicals that can destroy the activity of viruses which are present in the parent plant. Tobacco mosaic virus, mixed with extracts from tobacco seeds, was inoculated into healthy tobacco plants; the virus did not cause an infection.

This chemical barrier to virus transmission through the seed enables us to start afresh with annual crops that are grown from seed every year. We can start off with plants that are virus-free, and by attacking insects that are carrying virus we can do much to protect the plants from infection as they grow.

But many of our most important agricultural crops are propagated by a vegetative process. A piece of the parent plant is removed—a corm or tuber, a shoot or branch or bud—and this is induced to form roots and grow into a new plant on its own account.

Whenever we raise plants in this way we hand on to the new plants a ration of any viruses that were present in the old ones. That is why we find so many virus diseases established in strawberries and raspberries, potatoes, dahlias, anemones, and other plants that are grown from 'cuttings' of one sort or another.

Moreover, there are many crops that go on producing their crops year after year. Orchard trees provide us with their fruit crops only after growing for several years; and they have to go on doing so for a generation or more. Other tree crops, such as cacao or cloves, dates and nuts, are also

borne on plants that have an active life extending over
years.

Even if these long-lived crops are not infected with a
virus disease to start with they cannot easily be protected
from subsequent infection from outside. A single insect
passing on a dose of virus is sufficient to infect a tree for
life.

Once this has happened we are faced with the problem
of cure as distinct from that of prevention. And curing a
virus disease in plants is very much more difficult than in
human beings.

Plants do not appear to have any system of self-
protection that can generate antibodies capable of destroying viruses. In animals the entry of a virus into the bloodstream sets off an alarm that results in antibody-production. The multiplying viruses find themselves up against an
army of defenders that can overwhelm them. By stimulating antibody-production artificially, with the help of
vaccines, we can protect ourselves from virus disease.
There seems to be no prospect of using vaccines in this way
in plants. Once a virus has found its way into a suitable
plant, it multiplies and remains throughout the life of the
plant. The plant is content to accept its fate without fighting back. There are no obvious natural defences that we
can stimulate artificially.

Although the plant cannot acquire any natural or stimulated immunity to virus infection through the production
of antibodies, it can display a different sort of immunity of
limited effect. When a virus has settled down inside its
host-plant it can act as a barrier to other viruses of a similar
type. The virus in occupation has taken over the cells in
which it multiplies, and there is no room left for late-
comers.

This blocking effect of one virus against another is
limited to viruses that are close relatives. The presence of
a virus already in the plant does not prevent the entry of
viruses of a different type. But despite this limitation,

occupational immunity can be a valuable method of protection. Like animal viruses, plant viruses often exist in many strains. These strains are essentially the same virus; they cause the same disease, but may vary in the severity of the symptoms that they cause. One strain may be so mild that it does not have any serious effect on the plant's health; a closely related strain may be so virulent that it will destroy the plant altogether.

If a mild strain is already in occupation it can protect the plant from damage caused by its more dangerous relative. Tobacco mosaic virus, for example, exists in many strains of widely-varying virulence. All have arisen from the original tobacco mosaic virus, and if one is present in the tobacco plant it can prevent the entry of any of the others.

This type of acquired immunity is of great value to the research worker; it helps him to decide whether two viruses causing different symptoms are in fact related. It could conceivably be put to practical use, enabling us to protect a valuable, long-standing crop against the threat of infection by a dangerous virus.

Nowadays we are relying more and more upon plant breeding to provide us with a measure of protection against all manner of pests and diseases. Viruses are no exception.

Some varieties and strains of plants are inherently more resistant to attack by viruses than are others. By selective breeding we can bring out this natural resistance and develop varieties of plant which are not troubled by attacking viruses. Virus-resisting potatoes, strawberries, and raspberries are now in widespread use. In the United States the introduction of virus-resisting sugar beet has enabled farmers to grow this crop in areas where curly-top virus had previously wiped it out.

The ability to resist a virus disease may stem from various characteristics of the plant. Sometimes a plant is affected so drastically by a virus infection that it dies completely, carrying the invading virus with it. If this virus disease is being spread by an insect the sudden collapse of the plant will deny the insect an opportunity of creating an epidemic. The source of virus disappears too quickly, before the insect has a chance of spreading it around.

Sometimes an invading virus will find that the plant into which it has penetrated is able to seal off the virus with a wall of dead tissue. Unable to make its way through the barrier of dead plant cells, the virus cannot infect the plant as a whole. It is held in isolated spots—like water in a holed ship, isolated by the bulkheads.

These virus-resisting characteristics of certain plant strains have been bred into commercial varieties and used as a practical method of avoiding virus infection.

If, despite all our precautions, a virus is able to establish itself inside a plant it is usually there for life. Until quite recently we could do nothing of any practical value towards getting rid of the virus from its host. But now things have begun to look a little brighter. There are indications that it may be possible to treat infected plants successfully in one way or another.

For more than thirty years it has been known that viruses could be destroyed by heating the plants in which they had established themselves. Sugar cane cuttings were cleared of two virus diseases by steeping them in hot water long enough to kill the viruses without damaging the cuttings.

This discovery, made in 1925, aroused remarkably little interest in a world where plant viruses were depriving us of millions of tons of food every year. In 1935 young peach-trees were cleared of 'yellow' virus by heating them for a fortnight at human body-temperature. Potatoes and tobacco were freed of different viruses in a similar way.

Since the end of World War II heat treatment has been used to some extent in practice to free infected plants. In Australia sugar cane is cleared of a virus by steeping the plants in hot water before planting.

At the Potato Research Institute in Patna, India, scientists have shown that a variety of potato called Phulwa, grown on the plains, is freed of leaf-roll virus during its storage in the fierce heat of the summer. But if the seed potatoes are kept under modern cold-storage conditions the plants that grow from them are often infected with leaf-roll; the virus survives in the potato during cold storage.

The effectiveness of heat-treatment depends upon the relative susceptibilities of virus and plant. Some viruses are easily destroyed; tomato spotted wilt virus, for example, is killed when it is heated at 42°C. for ten minutes. Mosaic virus, on the other hand, is a good deal tougher and can resist a much higher temperature.

Plants, too, vary greatly in their susceptibility to the effect of heat; it is often the plant which determines the success of heat-treatment rather than the virus. The virus which causes 'aster yellows' cannot be destroyed inside the aster, as the plant is easily damaged by heat. But this same virus infecting a periwinkle plant can be inactivated by heating the plant at 45°C. for a few hours. The periwinkle can survive this treatment unharmed.

This effect of heat upon plant viruses is important enough on its own account; it has already been put to practical use. But it is even more important in its implications; it has shown that plants can be influenced in such a way that they no longer permit the multiplication of viruses in their tissues. And if heat can inactivate viruses without destroying the cells in which they live, other things can presumably do the same.

Ultra-violet light, for example, will stop viruses penetrating into the surface cells of plant leaves. Some sort of cell-damage is done which prevents virus-multiplication, and the viruses are destroyed. As the plant recovers from the effects of ultra-violet radiation any virus that was present initially is no longer active.

This effect of ultra-violet radiation is confined to the

surface layers of the plant; the radiations do not penetrate
far enough to destroy viruses already established in the
tissues. Ultra-violet light is therefore less valuable than
heat for ridding plants of virus disease.

The rapid progress now being made with more penetrating forms of radiation has raised new possibilities.
X-rays and the gamma rays thrown off by radio-active
substances are known to inactivate viruses. But they may
do too much damage to the plant cells to be usable as a
practical curative treatment for virus diseases.

During the last twenty or thirty years immense strides
have been made in the use of chemicals against microbes
that cause plant and animal diseases. We have many effective fungicides for tackling the destructive blights and
mildews that can cause such havoc in agricultural crops;
we have innumerable chemical drugs for fighting disease
germs in the human and animal body. But in spite of our
resounding success against these microbes, we can still do
little against the viruses that cause so many diseases in
animals and plants.

The situation, in the case of plant viruses, is not quite
so hopeless as it seems. Chemicals have been found which,
while they do not necessarily destroy the virus, are able
to prevent its multiplying in the cell. In effect they protect
a plant from virus infection by rendering the virus ' sterile.'

Many natural substances have this virus-inhibiting
activity. They are found in the leaves of many plants,
including sweet william and carnation, and in many fungi.
Tissue fluids, such as blood, fruit juices, and milk, contain
proteins that are able to block the efforts of viruses to
multiply.

The anti-viral activity of these substances is anything
but straightforward. They seem to influence the virus indirectly by affecting the metabolism of the cells in which
it multiplies. The effectiveness of an anti-viral substance
depends upon the nature of the host rather than the virus
it is to inhibit. Juices pressed from plant leaves, for

example, will inhibit a virus that attacks another species of plant, but will have no effect on the same virus attacking the plant from which the juices came.

Some substances have been used experimentally as anti-virus sprays in crop protection. These chemicals are applied like insecticides and fungicides. But they act in a fundamentally different way. Insecticides and fungicides lie in wait on the surface of the plant or circulate in its tissues, and attack the insect or fungus spore immediately. But the anti-viral chemical is more indirect. It does not destroy the virus that is brought to the plant, but must penetrate with the virus and accompany it to the tissue cells in which the virus plans to multiply.

Many virus-inhibiting chemicals are substances with molecules almost as large as those of the virus itself. And, like the virus, they can penetrate only through a wound in the surface layers of the plant. If the virus makes its way into the plant through damaged surface tissue an anti-viral chemical that had been sprayed on the plant could make its entry in the same way too. And it would prevent the virus from multiplying.

But if, as is much more likely, the virus is injected by an aphid the anti-viral chemical will not influence the infection at all. It will remain on the outside of the leaf.

The value of this type of anti-viral spray on plants is therefore limited; it can protect the plant against those viruses which are spread by physical contact, rather than by an insect.

One of the worst virus infections of this type is the mosaic disease that affects tomato plants. The virus is the same as that which causes tobacco mosaic disease. It is extremely infective and is passed from one plant to another on the fingers of gardeners tending the plants. Often the virus is brought into a greenhouse in the tobacco of a cigarette, which may be heavily infected with virus of mosaic disease.

Experiments carried out at the John Innes Horticultural Institute have shown that the spread of tomato mosaic disease can be kept down by spraying the leaves of plants with milk. The anti-viral substance in milk penetrates into the plants through wounds made during handling, accompanying the virus that enters too, and preventing its multiplication in the plant cells.

Milk-spraying has cut down infection from 100 per cent. to 5 per cent., and with a variety called Potentate can prevent infection altogether.

This successful attack on plant viruses with the help of anti-viral substances does something to make up for the plant's fatalistic attitude towards virus attack. The plant does nothing to protect itself by generating antibodies; but there are indications that we can now bring anti-viral chemicals in to help.

13 | All Shapes and Sizes

For nearly half a century the virus lived only in the imagination of man. From the time of Iwanowski's 'discovery' of the virus in 1892 almost until the outbreak of World War II the existence of virus particles had to be taken on trust. We knew that viruses must be hidden in the infective sap of diseased plants and in the blood of victims of smallpox, yellow fever, and other diseases; but we could not see them. We studied the idiosyncrasies of viruses and worked out methods of fighting them. Yet, until 1938, we had little direct information about the shapes or sizes of these invisible microbes. One or two of the largest ones had been photographed with the help of ultra-violet light. But the rest were hidden away from human view, secure in a world of smallness into which rays of visible light could not penetrate.

In 1938 a new phase of virus research began; the first photographs of virus particles were taken with the help of the newly-devised electron microscope. After forty-six years of struggle against an invisible enemy scientists could at last see the incredibly small organism they had been fighting.

Since 1938 the electron microscope has become an instrument familiar in virus research; it has been making up for lost time, and has laid bare many details of virus anatomy. In less than twenty years we have amassed a store of information about the tiny 'germ' that lurked unseen in its micro-world for so long.

Nowadays we accept without question the fact that the virus is a discrete particle, a midget entity. Seeing is believing. We think instinctively of our viruses as tiny organisms that can invade living cells and multiply to cause disease. Whenever we are assailed by an unusual illness we are apt to pin the blame on an unidentified virus. It comes as something of a shock to recollect that this familiar scapegoat of our modern, health-conscious world has been with us in recognizable form only since the time of Munich.

The boundaries of the virus world were established originally on an arbitrary basis. Viruses were regarded simply as organisms that could not be detected through an ordinary microscope using visible light. This meant in effect that viruses were smaller than about 250 millimicrons in diameter. Visible light waves are too long to resolve the detail of any object smaller than this. Viruses therefore live in a world made invisible by the limitations of light waves that enable us to see.

As things have turned out this boundary set by the wave-lengths of visible light almost coincides with a boundary between two different forms of living thing. On one side, large enough to be seen in visible light, are bacteria and related organisms capable of independent life; on the other side are the viruses, which differ fundamentally from bacteria in that they come to life only inside a suitable living cell.

In studying these ultra-microscopic virus particles we are not merely examining smaller editions of the ' normal' germs we know. We are seeing a type of organism entirely different from anything that exists in our world of visible light. We are prying into a world peopled by apparently inanimate particles that can come to life.

The upper size-limit of the virus world, set by the resolving-power of the optical microscope, is small indeed. Yet we now know that virus particles cover a wide range of sizes below this boundary of sight.

With the help of the electron microscope we can now take measurements of virus particles directly from their photographs. Viruses can also be measured in other ways and the results from different techniques have shown encouraging agreement. We can now be certain that our estimates of the sizes of different virus particles are correct within reasonable limits.

One of the earliest techniques of virus measurement made use of special filter membranes in which the pores are of carefully graded sizes. Liquid containing the virus particles is allowed to flow through the membranes; by assessing the infectivity of the liquid passing through filter membranes of various grades it is possible to estimate the size of the virus particles. This method of virus measurement sounds simple enough in theory; but in practice it is extraordinarily difficult.

Another technique for measuring viruses depends upon the rate at which the particles 'settle out' from a liquid in which they are dispersed. When a virus-containing liquid is whizzed round in containers fixed to a rapidly-spinning rotor centrifugal force acts as a super-gravity. The virus particles move slowly through the liquid, collecting on the outermost surface of the inside of the container.

This technique is used for concentrating viruses; but by measuring the rate at which a virus settles out it is also possible to estimate its size and shape.

These filtration and centrifugal techniques are still being used in virus research. But they do not compare in elegance or importance with the electron microscope, which can give us a permanent visible record of the virus. With the help of this superb modern instrument we can study the detailed structure of each virus particle at our leisure.

The electron microscope enables us to 'see' particles as small as five millimicrons in diameter. With its aid we can explore the hidden region, ranging from the smallest germs to individual molecules of matter.

Within this region the electron microscope has shown us how very different one virus can be from another. The largest particles lie on the borderline between visible and invisible; some of them can in fact be detected through a good optical microscope. The psittacosis virus is about 275 millimicrons and the vaccinia virus 200 millimicrons in diameter. Both can be seen as specks shining against a dark background.

Most viruses, however, are less than 100 millimicrons in diameter and are well out of the range even of a microscope using ultra-violet light. *Herpes simplex* viruses are about 50 millimicrons; foot-and-mouth virus is 15 and poliomyelitis 12 millimicrons. These are the smallest animal viruses known.

Until we began to probe the detailed structures of these viruses, there was a tendency to assume that viruses would belong to a fairly well-defined type of organism. But, in fact, they show tremendous variations among themselves. In size alone, for example, viruses range from the 12 millimicrons of poliomyelitis to the 275 millimicrons of psittacosis; this is a twenty-three-fold difference. To a polio virus, a psittacosis virus would look as big as an elephant looks to a small dog. And the finer details of the physical build of virus particles are as different, one from another, as we find among the creatures of the animal world.

Since 1938 the electron microscope has undergone continuous improvement and refinement, and it can now provide us with a wealth of detail on virus structure. But there are many problems involved in using the electron microscope, and the study of viruses with its aid is not so simple as it sounds.

In place of visible light the electron microscope uses a stream of electrons which behaves like waves. The electron stream flows inside a vacuum chamber, so that the specimen itself is in a vacuum. This means that it is inevitably dehydrated; any water inside it must evaporate in the vacuum. The object photographed in the electron microscope is therefore a desiccated skeleton of the original specimen.

Also the electron stream cannot pass through glass in the way that visible light passes through a microscope slide. The specimen in an electron microscope must be supported on a wafer-thin film of collodion that permits the electrons to continue on their way.

To add to these difficulties, the specimen is normally a mixture of virus with bits and pieces of extraneous cell material. It is not easy to detect the virus and to separate it from the other matter. Sometimes the virus particles have a characteristic and easily recognized shape; often they are formless blobs that cannot be distinguished from other shapeless objects in the specimen.

Despite these difficulties, hundreds of virus photographs have now been taken, at magnifications of 100,000 times and more. We can see a virus particle 'blown up' to a size comparable with a human being magnified until he is 100 miles high.

In recent years new techniques have been devised which make the electron microscope even more effective in our study of the virus. We can, for example, stain viruses just as we stain specimens under the normal microscope. Different parts of the virus take up the staining material in different amounts, so that the fine detail shows up more clearly in the photograph.

The three-dimensional structure of virus particles can be enhanced by shadowing the specimen with a film of metal. A cloud of metal atoms is blown sideways across the specimen, so that a thin layer of metal builds up on the 'windward' side of the particles. A metal-free shadow is left on the leeward side. When a metal-shadowed specimen of this sort is photographed in the electron microscope the virus particles stand out from their background like boulders on a beach at sunset.

Dr Robley C. Williams, of the University of California, has devised a process for freeze-drying virus specimens before they are put into the microscope. Instead of becoming distorted as they are dehydrated, the virus particles retain their original shape and give a truer picture. Viruses thought to be spherical, for example, are often seen to be polyhedral when photographed after freeze-drying.

Another drying technique developed by Thomas F. Anderson preserves the true shape of virus particles in a similar way; it has enabled us to photograph bacteriophages as they attach themselves to their host-cells by their tails.

The discovery of these shape-preserving processes has altered our ideas on virus sizes. When viruses are photographed in the normal way they are often flattened by the distortion caused by evaporation of water from the specimen. The sizes of the particles, as shown by measurement of their photographs, are larger than they ought to be. The influenza virus, photographed after freeze-drying, is actually one-fifth smaller than it appears in an ordinary electron micrograph.

Most virus particles are comparatively simple in shape. They fall into three main classes. Some are spherical or polyhedral, others are 'rods,' and others 'tadpoles.'

Animal viruses are mostly spherical, near-spherical, or polyhedral. Photographed in an electron microscope, they look like puff-balls growing on a lawn. In size animal viruses vary from the 275 millimicrons of psittacosis to the twelve millimicrons of polio.

The influenza virus is unique in having two distinct shapes. It can be seen as little balls about 100 millimicrons in diameter, and also as long threads of about the same thickness. These thread-like particles are often 100 times as long as the virus balls; they can be seen through an optical microscope when illuminated against a dark background.

Bacterial viruses, or bacteriophages, are tadpole-shaped. Some of their tails are so small as to be almost invisible; others are three times as long as the head.

Plant viruses, which can so often be obtained in crystalline form, tend to be rod-like in shape. The tobacco mosaic virus, for example, looks like a thin glass bar. It is about 275 millimicrons long and fifteen millimicrons wide.

Despite the wide range of virus sizes, therefore, the external appearance of the particles is not particularly varied or exciting. But our use of the electron microscope and of other new techniques has enabled us to go much farther into the details of virus structure. And the deeper we probe, the more remarkable do our discoveries become.

It is a characteristic of all viruses that they cannot live an independent life. They can multiply only inside a living cell. This fact, together with the obviously chemical properties of crystalline viruses, has encouraged the belief that viruses are best studied as 'mineral' rather than ' animal.' Yet the electron microscope has shown that some of the larger animal viruses, and the bacteriophages that attack bacteria, have many of the superficial attributes of a self-contained organism. They are, for example, enclosed by a membrane that can be compared with the cell-wall of a free-living bacterium.

When the psittacosis virus is dried before being put into the electron microscope, it shrinks and shrivels like a plum being turned into a prune. Its photograph shows that the virus is surrounded by a skin that collapses inward when the water is removed. The folded skin is left clinging to the core of dehydrated virus.

In 1948 photographs of vaccinia viruses were taken by Dr I. M. Dawson and Dr A. S. McFarlane, of the National Institute for Medical Research, London. Magnified 100,000 times, the virus appears as a rounded cube, similar to a lump of sugar. Its surface is rough and pitted as though the virus itself was made up of many tiny granules. Sometimes long filaments are seen alongside the virus particles, formed as though by chains of particles that have broken away from the virus itself.

The mottled surface of the vaccinia virus enhances its

resemblance to a lump of sugar. But the tiny bumps that roughen the surface of the particle are arranged to form a pattern of regularity that is quite different from the random packing of the separate crystals in a sugar lump. There is a suggestion of order in the way in which the granules forming the virus particles are held together. The virus appears to have a well-defined internal structure of its own; it shows signs of being built from smaller parts, and in this respect approaches the design of a self-contained organism such as a bacterium.

Dawson and McFarlane took photographs of vaccinia viruses which had been treated with pepsin, one of the ferments of the human digestive system. Pepsin breaks down the protein that we eat, turning it into simpler substances that can be absorbed through the stomach wall. Its effect on the vaccinia virus was to strip away much of the outer substance of the particle, leaving a mass of dense matter surrounded by a collapsed and folded membrane. Like the psittacosis virus, the large vaccinia virus is not a simple, homogeneous particle.

These researches on the larger animal viruses suggest that these almost-visible particles may act as a bridge between the large, independent, free-living cells of bacteria and the simpler, more chemical-like plant viruses. They are almost independent organisms, but not quite. In size they are not so much smaller than many bacteria, which are sometimes only 700 millimicrons in diameter—less than three times the diameter of a psittacosis virus.

Much of our recent information on the detailed structure of viruses has come from a study of bacteriophages, the viruses that attack bacteria. We now know that these tadpole-like particles are built in the form of a miniature syringe. Surrounded by a sturdy membrane, the bacteriophage has a hollow tail and a well-filled head.

The capsules of bacteriophages can be burst by subjecting the viruses to a treatment called osmotic shock. A solution of salt containing bacteriophages is diluted rapidly with water. Under this treatment the head of a bacteriophage is distended suddenly and will often burst. The contents of the head are released into the salt solution, leaving an empty 'ghost' virus behind consisting of a head membrane with the tail still attached to it.

Since 1935, when W. M. Stanley isolated tobacco mosaic virus from infected plants as a crystalline chemical, plant viruses have been the focus of an immense amount of research. In many respects they are simpler organisms than the animal viruses or the bacteriophages. The fact that they can be obtained as crystals means that they can be subjected to the familiar processes of chemistry. They can be concentrated easily and purified, and there is no danger to the scientist who handles them.

The ability to form a crystal is often regarded as an inherent characteristic of an inanimate chemical. Crystals are built up by millions of atoms or molecules of a substance which align themselves together in a strict geometrical pattern. Rank upon rank, layer upon layer, the particles fit in beside each other forming a precise, compact association of particles. As the atoms or molecules continue to take up their stations in the edifice the crystal grows. It becomes large enough to be seen by the naked eye. Then, as more particles are added to it, it becomes perhaps an inch or two in length; then it may grow farther: a foot, two feet, or even more. There is no limit to the size a crystal may attain if there are sufficient particles available to go on adding to the structure.

No matter how big it grows, the crystal will retain the basic shapes that are laid down by the arrangement of the millions of particles from which it is made. The geometrical precision of a crystal is a consequence of the ordered arrangement of the particles from which it has been formed. It is a reflection of the similarity between the particles themselves.

In a crystal of plant virus millions of individual viruses have aligned themselves in a regular, ordered way. By forming a crystal the particles have carried out a self-concentration process, providing us with a pure and convenient mass of virus material.

The fact that plant viruses can get together as crystals in this way is an indication of their structural simplicity. Complex organisms, such as bacteria, do not form crystals. Each bacterium cell is an individual with a personality of its own; it does not have the simple chemical structure that can make it a replica of its colleagues.

Seen through the electron microscope, an individual plant virus is apparently a simpler thing than an animal virus or a bacteriophage. The tobacco mosaic virus is a long, thin rod. It does not have a membrane, nor is there any obvious subdivision of the particle into sections with different functions. There is no 'head' or 'tail' as there is in the bacteriophage.

The simplicity of the plant virus has attracted scientists who see in it a convenient way of studying the mysteries of the virus's 'near-life.' And many techniques are being evolved for exploring the plant virus particle in detail.

For years scientists had to be content with a sideways view of the tobacco mosaic virus seen through the electron microscope. It was identified as a long, thin rod. But nobody knew what it looked like in cross-section.

In 1952 Robley Williams of the University of California devised a method of photographing the virus end-on. He subjected a solution of virus to sound-waves of very high frequency. When the solution was dried and the virus photographed Williams found that the rapid vibration had broken up the virus rods into little sections. Some of the bits of virus were standing on end, and at a magnification of 200,000 they were seen to be hexagonal in cross-section. The individual particles themselves, like the crystals formed when they get together, appear to have a precise geometric structure.

Since 1938, when the first electron micrographs of viruses were made, we have come a long way in our study of the shapes and forms of virus particles. But already we have gone much farther than this, and we are prying into the interior of these strange particles. We are seeking to understand what viruses are made of. We are trying to find out how they are related to the chemical structure of the living cell.

14

Inside the Virus

As we have gone on peering and prying into the detailed make-up of the virus particle one thing has become quite clear. Every virus studied so far contains a ration of two different types of chemical substance. The bulk of the virus particle consists of protein. But there is always a smaller amount of another substance—nucleic acid—associated with the protein in one way or another.

These two substances, protein and nucleic acid, are complex chemicals that are intimately associated with the chemical processes of life itself. They are essential constituents of every living cell; a virus particle can be regarded as a neatly packaged carton of the two most important raw materials involved in the chemical merry-go-round that goes on inside the living cell.

Nucleic acid is not a single distinct substance; the name is a generic one which covers several closely allied substances having a basically similar chemical form. Nucleic acid is involved in the mysterious processes that take place in the nucleus, the heart of the living cell. With protein, it is a raw material from which the cell constructs its chromosomes; these are the little thread-like bodies which control the pattern of heredity in cell-reproduction.

The nucleic acid carried by a virus particle is therefore a portion of matter that takes part in the fundamental processes of life.

The bulk of a virus particle, however, is protein. This is the veritable stuff of life, the substance from which so much of the living body is made. Protein, like nucleic acid, is not a single chemical substance, but a group of closely allied substances. All proteins are related one to another in their essential chemical structure. They are all extremely complex, with molecules constructed from thousands or even hundreds of thousands of individual atoms.

Protein forms the bulk of the matter of the living cell. It is the structural material from which the cell, and hence the body itself, is built. Hundreds of proteins are associated with one another in the protoplasm in which the living processes of the cell take place. Colonies of cells which we describe as tissues are largely protein; skin and muscle, hair and sinew, are concentrations of protein that have come from the protoplasm of the cells that made them.

This life-supporting protein is the bulkier constituent of the virus particle. With its partner, nucleic acid, it forms a self-contained chemical team, the virus, that can take over the life-processes of the living cell.

Nowadays we know something of the way in which the two constituents are arranged inside virus particles. We have probed and dissected viruses and located the relative positions of protein and nucleic acid inside the particles.

Bacteriophages, those tadpole-like viruses that multiply inside bacteria, have been the subject of much of our modern virus research. With the help of the electron microscope we can photograph bacteriophages at work, and study their detailed structure.

As we have already seen, the bacteriophage is like a little hypodermic needle; attaching itself to the bacterium by its tail, the bacteriophage injects the contents of its 'head' into its victim. The shell of the bacteriophage is the protein part of the virus and the nucleic acid forms the contents of the 'head.'

This hypodermic tadpole structure of the bacteriophage was established largely as a result of electron micrographs

showing the viruses in action. But the finer details of the
bacteriophage's 'body' have been studied with the help of
a new technique using sub-atomic radiations.

It has long been known that radiations of various sorts
can disrupt the bonds that hold atoms together in the
molecules of more complex substances. In this way radiations can affect the processes that take place inside the
living cell. A fast-moving atomic particle bumping into
the nucleus of a cell may damage the delicate chemical
structures that carry hereditary characteristics. Radiations
coming from a radio-active substance, for example, can
bring about changes in the reproductive cells of an organism that may affect the personality of the offspring derived
from those cells.

This damage caused by radiations has been used since
1949 by Professor Ernest C. Pollard and his colleagues at
Yale University to probe the inner structure of virus particles. Streams of deuterons coming from a cyclotron were
allowed to bombard bacteriophages, and the effect of the
radiations on various properties of the viruses was studied.

If the deuterons are peppering the virus particle indis-
criminately and at random the number of 'direct hits' on
any section of the particle will be proportional to the size
of the section. The bigger it is, the more often it will be
hit. An elephant, for example, will be hit by more rain-
drops in a thunderstorm than will a horse.

If we assume that each direct hit causes damage to the
structure of the section of virus that it enters, we can
estimate the size of that particular section relative to the
size of other ones. If we could not see the elephant or the
horse we could estimate their relative sizes by measuring
the amount of water that each animal collected.

Professor Pollard studied the effects on different characteristics of the virus of deuteron-bombardment. And
by comparing the effects he could estimate the relative
sizes of the parts of the virus that were concerned with
various characteristics. The ability of the virus to repro-

 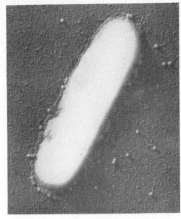

COLON BACILLUS

(*Left*) Disintegration under attack from T2 bacteriophages.

(*Right*) Attack by T1 bacteriophages.

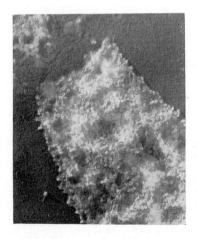 

Photos Dr R. W. G. Wyckoff

BACTERIOPHAGE FORMATION

(*Left*) T4 bacteriophage particles which have formed inside an invaded bacterium.

(*Right*) Particles appearing from a mass of protoplasm that has come from a destroyed bacterium.

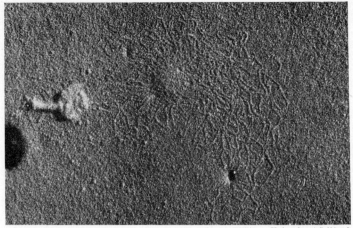

THE GHOST OF A VIRUS

This extraordinary electron micrograph shows a mass of nucleic acid threads which have been spilled out from the 'head' of a bacteriophage, leaving the empty protein shell.

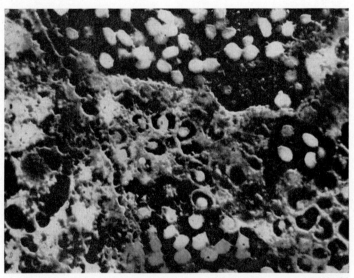

VIRUS FORMATION

This section, cut from an infected cell, shows particles of virus (*Molluscum contagiosum*) in an advanced stage of formation.

duce inside bacteria was, for example, extremely sensitive to deuteron-bombardment. The ease with which this characteristic was damaged indicated that it must be represented by a large section of the virus's ' body.' This corresponds to the nucleic acid 'filling' inside the head of the bacteriophage.

By altering the density of the beam of deuterons used to bombard the virus Professor Pollard was able to estimate the thickness of different 'behaviour units' in the particle. A thin unit, for example, might allow all the deuterons to pass through it without causing any damage at all. But, as the density of the radiation beam is increased, a thin unit of this sort becomes increasingly liable to suffer damage. By measuring the effect on different virus characteristics of increasing the density of the deuteron beam, it is possible to estimate the thickness of the corresponding regions in the virus 'body.'

Modifications of the bombardment technique gave even more precise information about the internal structure of the virus particle. The volumes of different behaviour units could be estimated, and the depth at which they were situated. Gradually a picture of the bacteriophage was built up, showing how the various behaviour units are distributed about its tadpole body.

The ability of the virus to infect bacteria is the most sensitive of all its characteristics. The part of the virus responsible for this property takes up about one-fifth of the total volume of the virus particle. It is long and thin in shape and is believed to be coiled up into a ball. This is the nucleic acid that is packed away inside the virus's head.

This infective portion of the virus was shown to lie about fifteen millimicrons below the virus's surface. It is covered by the shell of protein that extends to form the tail. The tail itself is only fifteen millimicrons thick, which confirms that it cannot contain any of the infective nucleic acid charge.

The point of the virus's tail is tipped with a chemically active plug which is able to dissolve a hole in the wall of the bacterium to which it becomes attached. The plug is about eight millimicrons long and eight millimicrons thick.

Although this picture of a bacteriophage is over-simplified and idealized, it is a remarkable example of the way in which modern scientific techniques can reach into the world inhabited by these smallest of all living things. We can visualize how these virus tadpoles go about their business, just as though we could watch them swimming in a goldfish bowl. Yet they are so small that 50,000 of them arranged in single file would hardly be as long as a normal tadpole.

Other types of virus are now being studied with the help of radiations of one sort or another. Ultra-violet light has shown, for example, that the infectivity of a virus is not exclusively the concern of the nucleic acid. The protein has some influence too.

At Columbia University, in the United States, Councilman Morgan and his colleagues have used techniques of incredible precision to cut sections through virus particles inside a cell. The specimen containing virus-infected cells is embedded in transparent plastic, and wafer-thin shavings are cut from it with a mechanically operated glass-bladed knife. As the shavings fall from the specimen they are collected on the supports used in the electron microscope.

In this way sections have been cut through the centre of *herpes simplex* viruses inside the nuclei of cells. The virus appears to be an almost spherical particle about 70–130 millimicrons in diameter, with a central core of only 40–60 millimicrons. These cross-section photographs suggest that the *herpes simplex* virus in fact has an outer membrane surrounding it when it is in the cell nucleus. In the cytoplasm which surrounds the nucleus the *herpes simplex* virus is even larger, with two distinct membranes instead of one.

It seems likely, therefore, that *herpes simplex* virus has some sort of complex internal structure during its cycle of activity inside the cell. Its outer membranes are similar to those which have been seen in vaccinia and influenza viruses.

This complex internal structure of animal viruses is supported by experiments carried out at the Rockefeller Foundation Division of Medicine and Public Health. Dr Delphine H. Clarke devised a method of separating viruses into different constituents each carrying separate characteristics of the virus itself.

Viruses from infected mouse brains were separated electrically into three distinct portions. One carried the ability to infect mice, another was able to combine with certain blood constituents, and the third made red blood cells clump together.

Dr Clarke suggests that an animal virus of this sort can be visualized as an orange. The whole fruit represents the complete virus, which is fully infective.

With the rind removed, the remainder of the virus cannot cause infection. The rind is the portion that supplies the power to infect. The inside of the orange can cause red cells to clump together and will combine with the blood constituents. Each segment of the inside of the orange can combine with the blood constituents, but has no power to infect or to cause red cells to clump together.

The obvious complexity of some of these animal viruses has made their investigation more difficult than that of other viruses. Much of the fundamental research on virus structure has been carried out on plant viruses, which are so much simpler in structure, and are easier to handle experimentally.

At least twelve different viruses have now been separated as pure homogeneous crystals from infected plants. All have been analysed and appear to contain only nucleic acid and protein. They differ one from another in the proportion of protein to nucleic acid, and the characteristic

shapes of the virus particles seen through the electron
microscope are different.

The crystallinity of plant viruses has enabled us to study
their detailed structure with the help of X-rays. When
X-rays are allowed to pass through crystals the tiny waves
of radiation forming the rays are turned aside by the atoms
and molecules inside the crystal. By measuring the characteristics of this 'diffraction' of X-rays we can discover
much about the arrangement of the particles forming the
crystal. This technique of X-ray diffraction has been used
with great success in many fields of scientific research. It
has now given us much information about the interior
organization of plant viruses—notably the tobacco mosaic
virus.

This little rod-shaped particle is about fifteen millimicrons in diameter and reaches a length of as much as
300 millimicrons. It weighs fifty million times as much as
an atom of hydrogen, and consists of almost pure protein.
Only 6 per cent of the tobacco mosaic virus is nucleic acid.

The comparatively small charge of nucleic acid is
carried by the tobacco mosaic virus in the centre of the
particle. It runs like a long thin core through the middle
of the virus rod. The particle as a whole has some resemblance to a piece of heavily-insulated electric cable; the
proteins form the thick outer insulation, with the thin core
of nucleic acid running through it like a fine copper wire.

With the help of X-rays we have learned something of
how the protein itself is arranged round the nucleic acid
core. The weight of the protein indicates that it may consist of millions of atoms joined together to form a giant
molecule. But there is evidence that the virus protein is,
in fact, built up from smaller protein units.

If all the atoms in the protein were joined on to one
another the virus particle would be little more than a
single outsize molecule of protein surrounding a nucleic
acid core. X-ray diffraction confirms that the protein shell
is constructed from smaller protein molecules, each con-

taining only a few thousand atoms. These units, which are identical or almost identical with one another, weigh only about 10,000–20,000 times as much as a hydrogen atom.

In 1955 Dr Rosalind E. Franklin, of Birkbeck College, London, worked out how these small protein units may be arranged in the tobacco mosaic virus particle. X-ray diffraction indicated that the virus is in the form of a spiral. Each protein unit lies like an almost triangular slab, fitting alongside its neighbours like a step in a spiral staircase. When thirteen of these sections are in position they make up rather more than a complete cross-section of the virus particle; the 'thirteenth' section fits above the 'first' one in each turn of the spiral, so that the hundreds of triangular protein units in the complete particle are arranged as a long continuous spiral.

Seen from the side, the virus particle looks like a compressed spring. Its surface is marked by screw-like grooves formed by overlying layers of the spiral. And inside the spiral container the narrow core of nucleic acid runs like the central pillar of the spiral staircase.

With the help of X-rays, therefore, we are revealing the inner secrets of the structure of plant viruses as effectively as we are probing into bacteriophages with atomic radiations. Much has already been learned, but there is plenty still to be done. How are the chains of atoms in the protein molecules arranged inside the virus particle? Where do the various groups of atoms lie relative to one another? How is the nucleic acid fitted in between the protein molecules?

As we try to answer these questions and to extend our knowledge of the physical make-up of virus particles, we are at the same time becoming involved in the chemistry of the nucleic acids and protein from which viruses are made. In these two aspects of virus research alone there is enough to keep a host of virus researchers busy for a hundred years.

15

A Way through the Wall

OUTSIDE the living cell a virus particle is nothing more than a little piece of complex chemical material. It does not breathe or eat, nor can it reproduce; it shows none of the normal attributes of life. But this inanimate particle of matter can bring about the manufacture of hundreds or even thousands of identical particles. All we have to do to make it multiply is to let it penetrate inside a suitable living cell. Often in a matter of minutes the cell will burst and the immense family of new viruses will appear. These viruses are, in their turn, mere particles of matter. They are as lifeless as the particle from which they came.

It is in this incredible multiplication process that the true mystery of the virus lies. Inside the host-cell something wonderful takes place, bridging the gap between one lifeless virus particle and its equally lifeless progeny. Hidden from human view behind the membrane walls of the cell, the virus particle takes on the normal living processes of the cell and redirects their efforts towards the production of viruses built to its own particular design.

This is the puzzle that so many scientists are trying to solve to-day. What goes on inside the cell that has been invaded by the virus? How does this extraordinary bit of matter persuade the cell to give up its normal work and destroy itself by building its living substance into virus particles?

The first step in the virus multiplication process is the penetration of the virus into the cell. Superficially, at least, there is a resemblance between this entry of a virus into its host cell and the fertilization of a female egg-cell by a male sperm during reproduction. The virus attaches itself to the cell-wall of its host and makes its way into the inside of the cell; the sperm penetrates an egg-cell by an almost identical process. The virus and the sperm are equipped with some sort of chemical mechanism that enables them to make their way through the coating which protects and encloses the living protoplasm of the cell.

A study of the fertilization of sea-urchins' eggs has shown something of the way in which this cell-wall penetration takes place. There is a substance in the coating of the sea-urchin's egg which interacts chemically with a corresponding substance in the sperm. When the two come together the coating-substance is destroyed and a hole is formed through which the sperm enters the egg.

The process can be likened to the opening of a locked door with a key. The sperm carries a chemical key that fits the chemical lock of the egg-cell wall. Together they permit the door to open. Like any lock and key, the cell-penetration substances are specific in their interaction. The 'lock' in the cell-wall can be opened only by the proper 'key.' That is to say, an egg-cell can be penetrated only by a sperm that carries the chemical key which fits it. This is Nature's way of preserving the personality of individual species. If an egg-cell could be fertilized by any sperm it chanced to meet uncontrolled cross-breeding could take place. But by providing every egg-cell with a chemical lock that is opened normally only by the chemical key of a sperm of the same species Nature ensures that the progress of evolution continues smoothly on its way.

When sea-urchin sperms are put into water from which sea-urchin eggs have recently been removed the sperms lose their ability to penetrate the egg-cell wall. The water is charged with 'lock' chemical that has seeped from the egg-cell walls. This interacts with the 'key' chemical on the sperms; when the sperms are subsequently brought into contact with egg-cells they can no longer unlock the cell-wall door. Their chemical 'keys' are fixed into 'locks' that have come away from the cell-wall and are floating freely in the water.

This seepage of 'lock' chemical from the cell-wall is one of the reasons for the prolific production of sperms that is necessary to ensure fertilization of comparatively few eggs. Many of the sperms are inactivated by the cloud of chemical that is seeping from the egg-cell. Only a few sperms manage to reach the eggs without being neutralized before they get there.

This 'lock and key' process is believed to operate in a similar way when a virus penetrates the living cell of its host. The bacterial viruses, for example, have been shown to carry a chemical 'key' in the tip of the tail, which combines with a corresponding 'lock' in the cell-wall of the bacterium. Solutions made from extracts of bacterial walls will inactivate viruses, just as water in which sea-urchin eggs are suspended will neutralize sperms.

This inactivation of viruses by cell-wall chemicals could conceivably be put to practical use in our efforts to defend ourselves against virus attack. The virus is able to penetrate a cell with the help of a chemical key; by isolating the chemical lock from the cell-wall we can neutralize the virus before it does any damage. Can we not find some chemical substance that could be injected into the human body and which would inactivate dangerous viruses before they were able to use their chemical 'key'? If we could make a synthetic chemical 'lock' into which the polio virus 'key' would fit, for example, we could prevent the viruses making their way into the cells in which they multiply.

Research has been carried out on this aspect of the virus problem, notably by Professor Sir F. M. Burnet and his colleagues in Melbourne, Australia. Most of the work has been done with influenza viruses.

Influenza makes its attack on man by invading cells in

the respiratory system. It is not easy to study the influenza virus directly in these cells. But the virus makes things easier for us by attaching itself to the red cells of the blood. It does not multiply inside these cells. But it adheres to their outer surfaces by a process similar to that which enables it to penetrate into the cells of the respiratory tract. We can study the attachment technique of the influenza virus conveniently by watching it in action on the surface of the red blood cell.

The influenza virus appears to carry a number of attachment areas on its outer surface. These little patches of 'key' chemical can combine with 'locks' in the wall of the red blood cell. But, as there are a number of 'key' patches on its surface, each virus can unite with more than one blood cell. An influenza virus can therefore act as a link that joins blood cells together.

This linking effect has been of the greatest importance in virus research. It brings about an easily visible change, called agglutination, in a suspension of red blood cells. In the presence of influenza virus the cells form little clumps that settle out.

This agglutination effect is brought about by viruses other than those of influenza. It has been adapted and modified in many ways; it enables us to estimate and identify viruses, and to distinguish between strains of individual virus species.

If a suspension of red blood cells is mixed with a lot of influenza virus the cells will clump together but in due course free themselves of the viruses that are clinging to them. The receptor patches have been destroyed on the cell surface, and they can no longer hold the viruses to them. These same cells can, however, absorb other types of virus, even though they remain inactive so far as the original influenza virus is concerned. Different viruses use different 'lock and key' links; the 'lock' that fits the 'key' of one can be destroyed without necessarily affecting other 'locks.'

This ability to destroy the receptor patches on a red blood cell is shared by substances liberated by certain micro-organisms. The germ of cholera, for example, manufactures a chemical that can destroy the 'lock' chemical in the red blood cell. This cholera-manufactured product has been described as RDE (receptor-destroying enzyme) by Professor Burnet. Like penicillin and other chemicals produced by micrò-organisms, RDE can be extracted and purified. It is a definite chemical substance, albeit a complex one.

The fact that RDE could destroy the virus-holding patches on the surface of a cell suggested to Burnet and his colleagues that it could perhaps be used as a protection against influenza. A dose of RDE injected into a person in contact with influenza might block the receptor patches on the sensitive cells and prevent influenza virus from entering the cells.

A series of remarkable experiments was carried out by Dr Joyce Stone, working in Burnet's laboratory. Dr Stone injected mice with RDE and found that they did in fact become immune to influenza virus. The RDE presumably destroyed the receptor patches on their virus-sensitive cells, and so prevented the virus pressing home its attack.

This method of immunizing has been used with other viruses as well; RDE can protect mice against certain polio-type viruses, and is effective against the virus of mumps. Unfortunately there is little prospect of using it as a practical method of protecting ourselves from virus diseases; the receptor patches on the cells, which are destroyed by the RDE, are regenerated in a matter of a day or two. The cells are then susceptible to virus attack again.

The actual processes that operate this lock and key mechanism of invading viruses are not yet understood. Cell-walls are constructed of incredibly complex building materials, with many different substances interwoven into the fabric of the membrane. It is believed that the influenza virus attacks the mucin-like substances that play an important part in the cell structure. Mucins are protein-carbohydrates; they are the slimy substances that we find in saliva and in the slithery coverings of snails and eels. The respiratory cells of human beings are protected by a layer of mucin; these are the cells which the influenza virus attacks.

The active areas on the influenza virus combine with corresponding patches in these mucin substances, and the virus sinks into the cell through the opening that is made. This mucin-destroying effect of the influenza virus can be shown in unusual ways. The virus can, for example, influence the sexual development of female rats; it attacks the sex hormone gonadotrophin, which is a mucin.

This job of penetrating the cell-wall of the host seems to be entrusted to the protein part of the virus. The tadpole-shaped bacteriophage, for example, clings on to its bacterial host by the tip of its tail. The nucleic acid charge remains inside the head of the virus until a hole has been made in the bacterium's coating. Then the nucleic acid is injected into the bacterium, leaving the protein shell of the virus behind.

The discovery of a method of bursting bacteriophages by osmotic shock enables us to remove the nucleic acid from the viruses, leaving only the empty protein shells behind. These nucleic acid-free ghosts of bacterial viruses can still attach themselves to bacteria. Lacking any charge of nucleic acid, they cannot induce any multiplication of virus inside the bacterium, but they can prevent its growth.

At the University of Colorado Medical Centre, Dr L. J. Tolmach and Dr T. T. Puck have used radio-active tracer-elements to study the chemical processes that control this union between the virus protein and its host-cell. The two bacterial viruses T1 and T2 which attack *Escherichia coli* were 'labelled' by persuading them to include a ration of radio-active phosphorus in place of their normal phosphorus. The radiations thrown off by this radio-active phosphorus could be detected easily so that the activity of the virus could be followed.

Escherichia coli was then subjected to various chemical treatments which would destroy different chemical structures on the surface of its cells. The labelled viruses were allowed to attack the treated bacteria, and their reactions were observed.

One thing that immediately became clear was that the radio-active phosphorus itself did not take part in the union between the virus and the bacterium. This confirmed that the protein part of the virus was responsible for penetration, and that the nucleic acid (which contains the phosphorus) was not directly concerned in this part of the virus's activities.

The experiments showed that T1 bacteriophage attacks the cell-wall of the bacterium through one type of chemical structure, and T2 needs an entirely different one. This chemical fussiness controls the specific nature of virus attack. It shows in a precise chemical way why one virus will attack a certain cell and another virus will not.

Whatever the chemical process used in cell-penetration may be, the result is usually the same. A door is opened in the cell-wall, and the attacking virus enters the environment which permits it to 'come to life.'

Inside a cell the virus finds itself in a world of bustle and activity. The living cell is the unit on which all living things are built. It is a small factory, packed with complex chemical substances all interacting with each other and undergoing the self-duplication processes that enable a cell to grow and split into its daughter cells.

Nowadays we accept the fact that all self-contained living things are composed of cells. The cell is a 'unit' of life, just as the atom is a 'unit' of matter. All the species of plants and animals—more than a million different ones are known—are constructed from cells living in close association with each other. Some creatures, like the primitive algæ or bacteria, are nothing more than single cells. Others, including the higher animals and man himself, are aggregates of billions of cells all doing a job of work that contributes something to the life of the living thing as a whole.

Cells vary greatly in shape and size, and serve in a variety of different ways. On average they are about one-third as wide as the thickness of a sheet of paper. In a plant or animal the work of the body structure is divided among many organs and tissues, each with a specialized task allotted to it. The cells forming these different organs are correspondingly diverse in function and form. In an animal the cells of the skin are flat and tough; the muscle cells are long and elastic, contracting and expanding to provide the body with the power of movement. In the blood red cells carry oxygen from the lungs to tissues, and help to dispose of waste products; white cells act as scavengers that get rid of unwanted material.

The life of the body as a whole is a composite life that comes from its countless cells. Each cell is a living unit that exists as one of a colony of cells all working together to form a delicately balanced whole.

Though the structure and behaviour of different types of cell can be so varied, there is a general pattern of design and activity that can be regarded as that of a 'typical' cell. The jelly-like contents of the cell is a complex mixture of hundreds or even thousands of chemical substances. This is the protoplasm, the substance of life itself. Floating in the middle of the protoplasm is a little jelly-filled balloon —the nucleus.

It is easy to think of the cell in terms of a simple, protoplasm-filled container that carries a ration of life. But, in fact, even the coarse structure of the cell, seen through a microscope, is incredibly complex. Inside the nucleus, for example, are two smaller balloons that are for ever changing their shape. These are the nucleoli, which serve in some way to carry food to the living units of the nucleus.

Inside the nucleus, too, are the chromosomes which carry the hereditary characteristics that are passed on to the daughter cells when division takes place.

The jelly-like substance that surrounds the nucleus contains a mixture of all manner of different components. In this outer-part of the cell protoplasm there are many types of crystals and fibrous particles. There are droplets of fat and pigment granules, little bits of food and pieces of waste material left over from the metabolic activity of the cell.

Nothing is ever at rest inside a living cell. The protoplasm is in a state of constant movement as the complex chemical processes of life go on. The most important event of all, not only in the life of the cell but in the life of every living thing that is made from cells, is the division of a single cell into two new daughter cells. This is the process which maintains the continuity of life; it is the basis of reproduction, the essential characteristic of life itself.

When the cell divides the chromosome threads inside the nucleus split lengthwise; the membrane around the nucleus disintegrates and the chromosome-halves separate and move to opposite sides of the cell. Then a new membrane forms around each set of chromosomes and eventually the cell divides. Each daughter cell carries away in its chromosomes a copy of the hereditary pattern of the cell.

Repeated over and over again, this process of cell division builds up the colonies of co-operating cells that we recognize as a bird or a holly-bush, an insect or a man.

As yet we know little about the intricate mechanisms that control this manufacture of new living matter inside the cell. Somehow or other the constituents of the cell are able to create replicas of themselves; they can build up a continuous supply of matter in their own image. And when the time comes the extra matter is shared out between two daughter cells of identical design.

This replication process that we recognize as a fundamental characteristic of life is essentially a chemical one. Simple raw materials reach the cell and seep through its walls. In man these raw materials are brought to the cells by blood and the body fluids. Oxygen comes from the lungs, water and other food-constituents from the digestive system. In plants, carbon dioxide is carried to the green cells by air that permeates the leaves; water and minerals are brought to the tissues via the roots that reach into the soil.

No matter how the living cell may receive its raw-material supplies, its function is the same. It turns these substances into the more intricate molecular designs that constitute the chemicals which take part in life.

In charge of the manufacturing processes that create continuous supplies of these life chemicals is the nucleus. The nucleus is the control centre of the cell. And the chromosomes that lie like little knotted threads in the nucleus are responsible for the hereditary characteristics that are handed down from a cell to its descendants. The chromosomes carry the blue-prints that show how new cells shall be made.

These chromosomes of the cell nucleus are now known to consist of two types of substance united in intimate association; they contain nucleic acid and protein. And these are the two substances from which we now know that viruses are made.

When the virus penetrates the wall of the cell it is making its way into a hectic chemical world controlled by the chromosomes in the cell nucleus. But the virus itself is a particle of matter constructed from the same two classes of substance as the chromosomes. As it sinks into the protoplasm of the cell it is like an extra bit of chromosome material interfering in the control mechanism of the cell. As soon as it arrives the virus throws the manufacturing processes of the cell completely out of gear.

16

The Virus multiplies

UNTIL quite recently many scientists believed that the virus multiplied in the same way as an ordinary living cell. It manufactured fresh supplies of living matter for itself and then divided its material assets between two daughter cells when it split in two. The only difference between a virus and a bacterium, for example, lay in the added dependence of the virus upon its host; the virus could not manufacture some of the things it needed for itself, so it had to parasitize a living cell which made these essential nutrients for it.

It is now fairly certain that this cell-type process does not account for the multiplication of the virus. It may be true that some of the larger animal viruses go through a life-cycle of this sort; there are indications, for example, that the vaccinia and psittacosis viruses have cell-like characteristics. But the smaller viruses, including bacteriophages and plant viruses, appear to multiply by a process that is all their own.

Much of what we know about the reproduction of the virus has come from a study of bacteriophages—the viruses that attack bacteria. The general pattern of multiplication is a familiar one. The virus, having made a hole in the cell wall where the tip of its tail is fixed to the bacterium, injects its charge of nucleic acid. The empty protein shell of the virus is left adhering to the bacterium and plays little further part in the proceedings. It has bored the hole and its job is done.

VIRUS SECTIONS

(Left) This little hexagonal-shaped particle is a fragment of tobacco mosaic virus seen in cross-section The virus was broken by high-frequency sound waves, some fragments—like this one—being left standing on end.
(×230,000.)

Photo Dr Robley C. Williams,
University of California

(Right) Herpes simplex viruses have, as shown in this electron micrograph, a complex internal structure. The virus particles have been sliced through the middle.

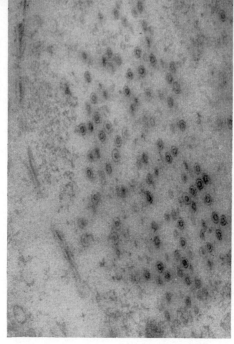

Photo Dr Councilman Morgan,
Columbia University

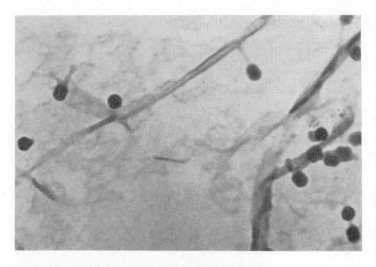

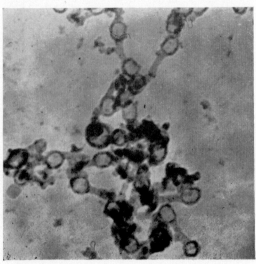

OSMOTIC SHOCK ON BACTERIO-PHAGES

The effects of this are seen in the 'heads' of virus particles. Above, the 'heads' are full. On the left they have been emptied of their nucleic acid.

Photos Dr T. F. Anderson

Inside the bacterial cell the charge of nucleic acid begins to make its presence felt as soon as it arrives. The manufacturing processes of the cell continue, but the control that was previously exerted by the chromosomes of the nucleus is now vested in the virus. This little bit of 'foreign' chromosome-like nucleic acid has become a cell-dictator.

Under the influence of the virus the production programme of the cell is changed. Instead of making new materials needed for its own continued existence and multiplication the cell begins to manufacture the substances needed for building new virus particles. The general type of substance is the same as that which would provide new chromosomes and other cell-material—protein and nucleic acid. But the detailed structure of the nucleic acid and protein are identical with those that form the virus particle. The cell is committed to a policy of self-destruction as it switches its activities to the production of virus material.

Once the virus has entered the cell it disappears completely. For a few minutes it is impossible to detect any virus particles inside the cell. Then, about half-way through the total 'multiplication period,' there are signs of virus particles in the cell. Their numbers grow until, after perhaps twenty minutes, the cell disrupts and releases 200 or more complete new virus particles. Each one is a replica of the virus that originally invaded the cell.

The disappearance of the virus after its entry into the cell of the bacterium indicates that the multiplication process is not a simple cell-like division of the virus particle. There is no steady increase of virus particles in the cell, as would be expected from a series of virus-splittings. Until half-way through the multiplication period there are no complete viruses in the cell at all.

A likely explanation of the virus's behaviour is that it disintegrates into a lot of smaller genetic units as it enters the cell. The nucleic acid of the virus can be regarded as

being built up into heredity-carrying units which, when
assembled, form the personality pattern of the virus particle. These units are analogous to the genes, the little
nucleic acid-protein units that are strung together to form
the thread-like chromosomes of a living cell. The resemblance is so close that we can be justified in calling the
little units of virus-material ' genes.'

As the nucleic acid from the virus enters the cell it
appears to break up into its constituent genes. Then these
genes or groups of genes begin to collect little pools of new
gene-material round them as the cell turns over its manufacturing processes to the virus-production programme.
Each pool continues to grow as new genes form identical
with the original virus-gene that provided the blue-print.
At the same time the cell is manufacturing protein that
will be needed to complete the self-contained virus particles. The composition of this protein is identical with that
of the protein-shell that was left outside the cell; the
nucleic acid is able to instruct the cell in the protein design
that will be needed.

At an appropriate stage, when sufficient new material
has been produced, supplies of new gene-material begin to
assemble forming nucleic acid 'chromosomes' identical
with the nucleic acid charge injected by the original virus.
These team up with units of newly-made protein, forming
the complete virus particles that are spewed out by the
swollen cell.

The apparently separate and distinct roles played by the
protein coat and the nucleic acid charge in bacterial
viruses has been confirmed with the help of radio-active
tracer elements. Nucleic acid in the virus can be 'labelled'
by replacing a small proportion of the phosphorus it contains with radio-active phosphorus; the protein can be
labelled in the same way by substituting some of its
sulphur with a radio-active sulphur. In each case the
chemical behaviour of the two substances remains unaffected; but wherever the nucleic acid or the protein go

as they take part in their virus activities, they can be detected and estimated by measuring the sub-atomic radiations emitted by the radio-active elements they contain.

At the Carnegie Institution, of Washington (New York), A. D. Hershey and M. W. Chase labelled the nucleic acid charge of bacterial viruses with radio-active phosphorus. They allowed the viruses to attack bacteria that had previously been destroyed by heat, and showed that the nucleic acid was ejected from the protein virus shells that fixed themselves to the coatings of the dead bacteria. The nucleic acid was easily destroyed by natural ferments, as the coatings of the dead bacteria were no longer able to protect the cell-contents from chemicals outside the cell.

Similarly nucleic acid injected by bacterial viruses into living bacteria could be destroyed by natural ferments if the bacteria were killed by heat after they were infected. Only the wall of the living bacterium could protect the nucleic acid part of the virus from destruction.

Hershey and Chase labelled the protein shell of bacterial viruses with radio-active sulphur. They allowed these radio-active viruses to attack bacteria and then stirred up the suspension of bacteria and viruses in a milk-shake mixer. The fast-moving stirrer broke off the empty protein shells of the viruses that were sticking to the infected bacteria; about 80 per cent. of the labelled protein was recovered from the liquid. But the nucleic acid had gone —it was inside the bacteria.

This vigorous treatment, though sufficient to break off the protein shells from the bacteria, did not interrupt the multiplication of the nucleic acid inside the bacterial cells. In due course a batch of virus progeny appeared, complete with their protein shells.

Perhaps the most remarkable thing about this virus multiplication process is the sheer efficiency and speed with which it operates. A typical bacteriophage, for example, will enter a bacterial cell, reorganize the intricate chemical processes going on inside the cell, and produce 200 replicas of itself in a matter of minutes. Not only does the nucleic acid charge injected into the bacterium stimulate the manufacture of more nucleic acid to its own design; it sees to the production of protein shells as well.

This 200-fold production of virus material can take place only if the necessary raw materials are available. Nucleic acid and protein are manufactured in every living cell from simpler chemical raw materials that permeate the cell-wall from outside. In the case of bacteria these substances are present in the ' culture-medium '—the food broth on which the bacteria grow.

The general similarity between the nucleic acids and proteins of normal cell material, and the nucleic acid and protein of the virus, might suggest that the virus draws upon ready-made cell substance for constructing its progeny. Both nucleic acids and proteins, for example, can be broken down into smaller units which could then be rearranged and put together again as the nucleic acid and protein of the virus. By doing this the virus could presumably avoid much tedious synthetic work which would be involved in manufacturing its materials from the simple substances that serve the cell as food.

In 1946 Seymour S. Cohen, of the University of Pennsylvania—a pioneer in the use of radio-active tracers for virus research—devised a series of experiments intended to throw some light on the problem of ' Where does the virus get its raw materials? ' Do they come from ready-made cell substance? Or are they synthesized from scratch, using the simple raw materials that surround the cell?

Cohen grew bacteria in two different flasks. The broth in one flask contained a small proportion of its phosphorus in the form of radio-active phosphorus; the phosphorus in the other broth was all normal, non-radio-active material.

After the bacteria had fed on the broth and multiplied, the colonies were removed from the broth, and switched about. The bacteria that had fed on the radio-active broth were transferred to the normal broth, and vice versa. The two colonies of bacteria were then infected with viruses. In due course the viruses entered the bacterial cells, multiplied, and released their progeny.

Cohen then measured the radio-activity of the two lots of viruses. He found that the viruses from the bacteria which had grown originally on radio-active broth had only about 30 per cent. as much radio-active phosphorus in them as the bacteria in which they had grown. They must have derived the rest of their phosphorus from the non-radio-active phosphorus in the broth surrounding the bacteria.

Similarly the viruses which had multiplied in non-radio-active bacteria (which had just been transferred to radio-active broth) had two-thirds as high a concentration of radio-active phosphorus as the broth which surrounded the bacteria.

Cohen's experiments showed clearly that, in the case of the phosphorus at least, the virus growing in the cell was drawing the bulk of its raw material needs from outside the cell in which it was multiplying. About two-thirds of the phosphorus came from the food-broth of the bacterium and about one-third from the phosphorus-containing substances of the cell itself.

For about ten minutes after infection there is no virus nucleic acid in the cell. During this time the virus is presumably getting the synthetic process under way. Once nucleic acid appears, however, it is produced about four times as fast as in the normal cell.

Other workers have since extended Cohen's research and have studied the phosphorus usage at different stages in the development of the bacteria and viruses. Growing normally, bacteria absorb the phosphorus they need at a rate corresponding to their rate of nucleic acid production. The phosphorus serves as a raw material for the nucleic acid that is an essential constituent of the cell.

As soon as the bacterium is attacked by a virus it begins

to absorb phosphorus much more rapidly than it did before. The extra supplies are needed for manufacturing virus nucleic acid.

Until these experiments proved that nucleic acid was manufactured from simple raw materials by the virus it had generally been assumed that the virus protein would be constructed from ready-made protein in the cell. After all, the cell itself is often adept at juggling the protein building-blocks, the amino acids, which it receives from outside sources. Human tissue cells are, for example, supplied with amino acids formed by the breakdown of protein constituents in food. From these amino acids the cells reconstruct the protein to their own designs. Why should not the invading virus do the same thing in the cell?

Frank W. Putnam and Lloyd M. Kozloff, of the University of Chicago, carried out experiments using radio-active nitrogen to trace the source of protein, much as radio-active phosphorus was used to follow nucleic acid production. They found that, once again, the virus was working on its own; it drew most of its raw materials for protein-production from the simple nitrogenous materials outside the cell. Only 5–25 per cent. of the nitrogen of the virus protein comes from nitrogen-containing substances already present in the cell.

Using radio-active phosphorus as a label for the nucleic acid in the virus, Putnam and Kozloff tried to find out what happened to the little packet of nucleic acid injected by the invading virus. Does it become part of the nucleic acid of all the new viruses? Does it appear in only one or two of the progeny? Or does it not take any direct part in the new viruses at all?

They found that about 40 per cent. of the original virus nucleic acid was incorporated in the virus progeny. Further experiments showed that the nucleic acid was distributed among the 200 or more descendants; each one had a ration of nucleic acid that came directly from its single virus ' parents,'

So, with the help of modern chemical and physical techniques, the nature of the bacterial virus multiplication routine is becoming gradually clearer. As it enters its host-cell the little charge of virus nucleic acid takes over control of the normal production processes of the cell; the activities of the cell are channelled towards production of new virus nucleic acid and protein, using raw material drawn largely from the outside of the cell. The speck of nucleic acid from the virus carries within itself the blue-prints that the cell must follow; these are the heredity-passing mechanisms similar to those that operate in the chromosomes of an ordinary cell.

In a typical bacterial virus, such as the T2 bacteriophage that attacks *Escherichia coli,* the entire process from infection to the bursting of the cell takes about twenty-four minutes. By opening infected bacteria at various stages after infection A. H. Doermann, at Cold Spring Harbour, has shown that the first twelve minutes of that period is taken up with the synthesis of virus substance. During this time there are no complete viruses in the cell. Nucleic acid and protein are being manufactured separately, but have not yet come together to form complete infective particles.

After the half-way point empty protein coats begin to appear. Then they are filled by nucleic acid charges, forming new virus particles that are complete and capable of infecting other bacteria. As the bursting-time approaches the bacterium is filled with more and more of these completed viruses. Then, after twenty-four minutes, the bacterium bursts and 200 or more new viruses are set free.

In the case of animal viruses our knowledge of the multiplication processes is very much more sketchy. But there are indications that the virus goes through a similar cycle of change inside its host-cell.

When two different strains of influenza virus are allowed to infect a living chick embryo the cells of the embryo may be entered by the two viruses simultaneously. If the viruses were to multiply by growing and then splitting in two it would be expected that two separate families of virus progeny would be released when the cell eventually burst. Each family would consist of replicas of the virus from which it came. But, in fact, it has been found that this sort of simultaneous infection gives rise to virus progeny that bear hereditary characteristics derived from both parents. They can be regarded as a form of virus hybrid.

If the multiplication of influenza viruses takes place by a process similar to that which is believed to operate in bacterial viruses this production of hybrids would be expected. As the virus enters the cell it breaks up into smaller sub-units, or genes; each gene then creates a pool of new genes to its own individual design. Then, when the time is ripe, the genes get together again to form complete virus particles.

If two influenza viruses are infecting a cell at the same time it might be expected that there would be some swopping about of closely-related genes. Particles would be built up containing some genes from one parent and some from another. Hybrid viruses would be formed, bearing some of the characteristics of one 'parent' virus and some of the other.

The technique of cutting extremely thin slices through infected cells has been of the greatest help in following the multiplication process inside infected animal cells. W. H. Gaylord and Joseph L. Melnick, using this method, have followed changes in the viruses of mouse-pox, vaccinia, and a human skin infection called *Molluscum contagiosum*. These viruses have distinctive shapes and are easily recognized in electron photomicrographs.

The development of new pox viruses of this type begins in the protoplasm surrounding the nucleus of the cell. Areas of dense material form near the cell-nucleus, as though the products of synthesis were collecting ready for conversion into virus. Then hollow spheres appear, increasing in number as the masses of dense material continue to expand. Groups of the little spheres begin to congregate;

they are larger than the mature virus—about 300 milli-microns compared with the 210–260 millimicrons of the virus.

As development of the virus continues the spheres are filled by material lighter than the surrounding substance. A little granule appears in the centre of the sphere; as it grows the sphere turns into a finished virus. The surrounding matrix disappears, presumably being used up as constructional material for the virus. Gradually the cell becomes filled with mature, infective viruses which are set free as the cell-wall bursts.

The practical difficulties of studying small animal viruses such as polio or yellow fever are so great that we know little about their multiplication processes. Dr J. L. Melnick and Dr J. B. LeRoy, of Yale University, have shown that polio virus is formed in the nuclei of susceptible cells. This can explain some of the characteristics of polio infection. The multiplication of virus in the cells of the spinal cord may make unusually heavy demands on the manufacturing processes of the nucleus; if the production cannot keep pace with virus requirements the entire cell structure will collapse and paralysis will follow.

The presence of polio virus in the nucleus could also explain the relationship between polio and fatigue. It is well known that over-tiredness will often increase the severity of a polio attack and encourage paralysis. Research has shown that the proteins of the cell nucleus are used up rapidly when the body is fatigued, and are replaced at a much slower rate. These heavy demands on nucleus protein, coming on top of the demands made by the virus, could well prove too much of a burden for the cell to support. The structure would break down, resulting in paralysis.

Councilman Morgan, at the Columbia University College of Physicians and Surgeons, New York, has shown that the viruses of cold sores begin their development in the nuclei of cells, and complete it in the surrounding protoplasm. While it is in the nucleus the virus is spherical and is surrounded by a single membrane. In the surrounding protoplasm it is three times as big and has a double membrane. The large vaccinia virus appears to have a cell-like structure, with a nucleus of its own.

Insect viruses are particularly easy to detect inside the cell. Their characteristic rod-shape enables us to recognize them easily in the mass of cell-material. K. M. Smith, at the Molteno Institute in Cambridge, using the thin-section technique, has been able to follow the development of viruses inside the nucleus of a silkworm cell.

After infection the nucleus of the cell grows larger and the chromosome-forming granules clump together into a network structure. At first there are no signs of virus; then little rods begin to protrude from the central mass.

These virus particles seem to form from fibrous material that thickens until it reaches virus-size. The rods are squeezed out from the nuclear material and begin to acquire their coating of protein. Gradually the particles build up into polyhedral crystals that are a feature of many insect viruses.

With evidence accumulating from so many different sources, it now seems reasonable to accept the 'splitting and reforming' theory of virus reproduction. During its residence inside the cell the virus breaks up into bits which manufacture more material like themselves. Then these come together again, joining up with newly-made protein to provide a family of new virus particles.

The time required for this mass-production job depends upon the nature of the virus. The viruses attacking colon bacteria can raise a family of 100–300 new viruses in thirteen to forty minutes. The influenza virus is more leisurely, releasing about fifty new viruses after remaining inside its host cell for five to nine hours. The pneumonia viruses of mice take even longer to complete their multiplication process; about sixteen new viruses are released after a 'gestation' period of fifteen hours.

17

Chemicals that live

WE have now reached the stage where we can outline an idealized picture of the virus and understand a little of its behaviour. Viruses which have been studied accurately and in some detail appear to consist of the two materials nucleic acid and protein, held together in intimate association one with another. The protein part of the virus is responsible for protecting the nucleic acid and for penetrating the wall of the cell that is to be invaded; the nucleic acid is the infective agent which enters the cell and brings about the production of new virus particles.

The fascinating thing about this two-part virus is that we can treat it as a chemical entity. Outside the cell-wall of its host the virus is to all intents and purposes a little bit of chemical. We can take it apart, separating its nucleic acid and its protein. We can analyse these two constituents and study their chemical structures, just as though we were investigating a natural drug or a new detergent. We can find out how the atoms are stuck together to form the molecules of nucleic acid and protein, and envisage what is happening when the chemical structures are affected by other substances.

Yet, as we carry out this scientific study of the virus, we know that we are probing the chemical intimacies of something that can come alive. Inside the test-tube a virus is subject to all the rules and regulations of normal chemical behaviour. But once inside its natural host-cell it enters into the activities that we recognize as life itself.

The virus is like a little piece of heredity-stuff that is living apart from its cell. It is a particle of chromosome material (containing the two essential chromosome substances—nucleic acid and protein) that is for ever on the look-out for a home in which to undergo the self-reproduction processes that create new living matter in the growing cell.

Once inside the cell the virus breaks down into its genes, which create supplies of material identical with themselves. As the genes are reassembled it is reasonable to suppose that little mistakes may occur. A misarrangement of the genes could result in a virus slightly different from the parent one. Superficial differences in behaviour would be imposed on the basically unchanged form of the virus as a whole.

In this way viruses undergo mutation; new strains are produced which are a breakaway from the characteristics passed on by the processes of heredity. Small changes of this sort would presumably occur more readily when the virus is growing in an unusual host-cell. It might be expected that an influenza virus growing in the embryo of an egg would find the raw materials of its surroundings a little different from those to which it is accustomed. Some chemical constituent may be lacking, or in short supply. The finished virus would then be slightly imperfect. It would be a mutant; a modified strain of virus formed by growing the virus in unfamiliar surroundings.

These characteristics of the virus in the cell—reproduction and mutation—are characteristics we associate with living things. In our attempts to understand the fundamental processes of life we find ourselves studying the phenomenon of heredity from these two points of view. But in the complex sub-micro world of the living cell the processes of reproduction are hidden in a maze of intricate chemical reactions that cannot easily be disentangled and subjected to precise analysis.

That is why the virus is becoming an important factor

in our modern researches on the mysteries of heredity. The virus is a clean-cut, pure, and often readily available chemical that is in many respects the embodiment of the chromosome which controls the reproductive processes of the living cell. We can subject the virus to the analytical techniques that are used for studying any ordinary chemical. And at the same time we can relate our discoveries to the behaviour of the virus as a living thing.

This strange Jekyll and Hyde existence of the virus has become one of the most intriguing mysteries to modern science. In the virus we have a chemical which can develop the power of life. By studying it as a chemical we can bring our researches close to the mysteries of living processes.

Modern biochemistry sees in the virus a link between the world of life and the world of no-life. This little particle enables us to study the self-reproducing substances of a living cell under the convenient and controlled conditions of the chemical laboratory.

The bulk of most viruses consists of protein; it belongs to the class of chemical from which much of our living matter is made. The virus protein is a close relative of the proteins that make up the muscle and hair, nails and skin, of the animal body.

These proteins are extraordinarily complex chemicals. But they are none the less chemical entities. They can be defined in their chemical structure as accurately as other chemicals can. We can say that albumen from an egg has its fundamental particle, its molecule, made up from certain atoms arranged in a certain way. If we could learn to arrange these atoms in the same way by chemical reactions in the laboratory we could make synthetic albumen in a test-tube. In the same way we could make synthetic flesh proteins, or synthetic hair. Or we could make the protein that forms the bulk of any specific virus particle. These things are not an impossibility to the scientist. They are merely so incredibly difficult as to leave us little hope of achieving any real success for many years to come.

We have not yet been able to build up a protein from simple chemicals by synthetic processes. We can make coal into nylon, and petroleum into rubber. But we cannot turn the simple chemicals from these raw materials into a protein. The arrangement of the carbon, hydrogen, nitrogen, and other atoms in the protein molecule is so bewildering in its complexity that we cannot yet compete with Nature in building the molecules from simpler chemical structures.

The fundamental particles, the molecules, of protein are characterized by their length. They are long and thin, with the constituent atoms joined together one after another in such a way that the composite molecule is like a string or thread. Many proteins have thousands of atoms joined together in this way in a single molecule.

In Nature the growing plant is able to construct the proteins that it needs from the simple chemicals it absorbs through its roots and leaves. Carbon atoms are supplied by the carbon dioxide that is absorbed from the air; hydrogen and oxygen come from water, and nitrogen from the nitrates that are drawn into the plant from the soil. These simple chemicals, with only a few atoms joined together in their molecules, supply the thousands of atoms that are built up into the long protein molecules manufactured by the plant.

In this ability to synthesize its proteins from simple chemicals the plant is cleverer than the animal. Animals depend upon proteins for much of their body structure; but they cannot make them from the simple chemicals used by the plant.[1] Animals depend upon plants to make their proteins for them. During digestion the plant proteins are broken down into smaller chemical units: amino acids. These amino acids are then absorbed into the blood-stream and rebuilt into proteins inside the living cells of the body.

Altogether there are only some twenty different amino acids used for protein-building in all living things. The vast

[1] See Chapter 1 of *The Fight for Food.*

range of different types of protein, from human muscle and skin to chicken feathers and the casein of milk, is made up from these comparatively few amino acids, which are joined together in different sequences and proportions in the protein molecules.

The fundamental particles of proteins can be compared with trains composed of twenty different types of rolling stock. The wagons represent the amino acids, which can be coupled up in any number, sequence, and lengths to form a train. Each train would be a different protein molecule.

The animal is able to uncouple the wagons of the train and couple them together again in any arrangement that it needs. But it cannot construct the wagons themselves from smaller units like girders and windows and wheels. These units represent the carbon and nitrogen and other atoms that come from simple chemicals like carbon dioxide and nitrates. Only the plant can use these for building amino acid ' wagons.'

In living cells the jelly-like protoplasm carries the phenomenon of life itself. Hundreds of different proteins take part in the chemical activities that go on in cell protoplasm. As cells divide and multiply supplies of protein are built up from the amino acids reaching the cells from the blood. Some of this protein is used for the construction of new chromosome-material, enabling the cell to pass on a ration of heredity-determining substance to its daughter cells.

The protein that forms the bulk of all viruses is therefore a class of chemical that is an essential constituent of all living matter. The other portion of the virus, the nucleic acid, plays an equally vital role in the life of the living cell.

All cells contain nucleic acids. Like proteins, the nucleic acids are chemically complex; and, like proteins, they can be broken down into smaller units consisting of simpler chemicals containing comparatively few atoms.

Just as the virus is formed by the union of nucleic acid and protein, so are the chromosomes of all living cells constructed from a union of these two substances. Chromosomes and viruses are close chemical relatives. Everything we learn about the chemical make-up of viruses tells us something about the chemistry of chromosomes too.

One of the most fascinating of all aspects of modern virus research is the study of virus behaviour in relation to its chemical constitution. Many viruses exist in different strains, the result of mutations which have altered the hereditary personality carried by the virus. As the virus is apparently little more than a piece of protein enclosing a core of nucleic acid, the heredity-pattern must somehow be imprinted on the chemical make-up of these substances. The difference between one strain of virus and another must be represented by a difference in the chemical structure of the virus constituents. Is it possible, therefore, to link up the personality of a virus with the arrangement of atoms in its molecule?

The purification of tobacco mosaic virus in 1935 by Dr Wendell Stanley made possible the study of this virus as a chemical. It could be subjected to all the processes of analysis that we use for finding out the arrangement of atoms in any ordinary chemical substance.

Since 1935 at least a dozen plant viruses have been isolated and purified as crystals. Animal viruses have been less co-operative; it was not until 1955 that the polio virus became the first animal virus to be obtained in crystalline form.

Meanwhile techniques of analysis have made immense progress, and it is now possible to see into the inner chemical structure of virus proteins and nucleic acids. We can assess the chemical differences between various strains of a virus, and see how these differences are reflected in the biological behaviour of the strains.

Tobacco mosaic virus has played a leading role in this research. The virus is comparatively simple to obtain in large quantities, and can be purified easily. Tobacco plants are not difficult to handle, nor are they unduly expensive as experimental testing units.

The tobacco mosaic virus exists in at least fifty strains. Under the electron microscope these all appear to be the same virus; they show no easily detected modifications in structure. Yet the diseases they produce in the tobacco plant all differ from one another in symptoms and effects.

These strains of tobacco mosaic virus have presented us with a first-rate opportunity of carrying out a chemical approach to the virus problem. They can be analysed and studied as ordinary chemical substances in the knowledge that differences in their chemical structures can be correlated with distinctive personality traits.

Already an impressive start has been made on this link-up between the chemical composition of the tobacco mosaic virus and its behaviour as a living thing. A detailed study of the proteins from several strains of the virus has revealed differences in their chemical composition.

With the help of up-to-date chemical techniques proteins can now be broken up into their amino acid units, and the amount of each amino acid estimated. It is therefore possible to assess the relative proportions of each of the twenty or so amino acids in any protein molecule; we can find out how many units of every type of " rolling-stock " there are in the protein " train."

Analyses of this sort carried out on several strains of tobacco mosaic virus have shown that there are variations in the amino acid content of different strains. One 'killer' strain of virus, which is fatal to the tobacco plant it infects, differs from a 'mild' strain in the amounts of two of the amino acids in the protein; one strain has 10–20 per cent. more of these amino acids than the other. Another strain is entirely lacking in two amino acids that are normally present.

An investigation of this sort, carried out on thirteen strains of tobacco mosaic virus, has shown quite definitely that the biological effects of any strain depends upon its protein structure; those strains that behave alike have proteins that are chemically similar.

Experiments of this sort have also been carried out on influenza viruses, and differences have been shown between the chemical structures of the proteins in Type A and Type B viruses. The two proteins contain the same amino acids, but the amounts of five of them differ between one virus protein and the other.

The proteins from bacteriophages that attack *Escherichia coli* have been analysed, and once again the biological behaviour of the viruses depends upon their protein structure. Two bacteriophages with distinct personalities have proteins that are different in amino acid make-up; bacteriophages that behave alike show little difference in protein structure.

Although we can determine the amounts of amino acids that are present in a protein molecule, this does not give us a complete picture of the protein structure. It tells us nothing, for example, of the sequence in which the amino acids are arranged.

This inadequacy in our knowledge is brought out by the fact that some plant viruses can be shown to have identical amino acid contents in their proteins. Yet they behave in very different ways. This could be due to limitations in our chemical techniques, which are not sufficiently accurate to detect small variations in the protein structure. Or it may be caused by differences in the arrangement of amino acids in the protein molecules.

The other half of the virus particle, the nucleic acid, has also been studied. At the University of Cambridge, Roy Markham and J. D. Smith analysed nucleic acids obtained from four strains of tobacco mosaic virus and four unrelated plant viruses. They found that the tobacco mosaic viruses contained nucleic acids that were very similar in chemical structure. But the nucleic acids from the other viruses were different.

Similar experiments with insect viruses and bacteriophages have indicated that this type of relationship is quite
general. Viruses closely related biologically have nucleic
acids that are very much alike; viruses that behave in
different ways have nucleic acids which are chemically
distinct.

Although these researches tell us only a little of what
we want to know about the chemical composition of the
proteins and nucleic acids in the virus, they have done
much to increase our understanding of the chemical processes of heredity. It seems apparent that the existence of
distinct strains of a virus is made possible by variations in
the chemical structure of both the protein and nucleic
acid. The mutation of a virus, with the production of a new
strain, may be caused by slight modifications that are imposed upon the virus by the cell in which it multiplies. It
is conceivable that some inadequacy in the supply of raw
materials would result in a shortage of one or more of the
amino acids needed for the proper construction of the virus
protein. The pool of genes that are accumulating new virus
substance inside the cell would have to make do with some
more readily available amino acid, or alter the blue-print
to omit an amino acid altogether.

The result of such behaviour would be to produce a
virus that was not quite identical with the virus that
invaded the cell. It would be essentially the same, but its
altered structure would provide it with an amended personality. It would be a new strain, a mutant.

We know nothing of the influences that control these
chemical modifications to viruses under natural conditions.
We cannot say how polio virus has developed its several
distinct and separate strains. Nor can we understand why
a particularly virulent strain of influenza should appear so
suddenly in 1918. We have no specimen of this virus
available to-day; we cannot analyse it and relate its
virulence to any chemical idiosyncrasies in the materials
of the virus.

It is perhaps a little easier to appreciate that mutation can produce new strains when viruses are multiplying in unfamiliar surroundings. The influenza virus in the hen's egg is called upon to generate new virus-substance from raw materials that are not quite up to human standards. The virus must make-do with the substances it finds, and the progeny are not quite what they ought to be. They are a new strain of influenza virus. They are sufficiently like the parent virus to stimulate antibodies in the human blood. But their behaviour is not the same as that of the normal influenza virus. They are better suited to producing more of their kind inside the cells of a hen's egg. These are the surroundings that can supply them with the raw materials they need.

These studies of the chemical structures of virus proteins and nucleic acids are of immense practical significance. We have begun to find a direct relationship between the biological activity of a virus and its chemical composition. With increasing understanding of the chemistry of the virus we shall be able to bring about changes in biological behaviour by carrying out deliberate chemical changes on the virus in the laboratory. In the knowledge that a certain chemical structure will bring certain biological consequences, we shall be able to exert some control over the processes of mutation. The discovery of desirable viruses, such as the 17D yellow fever virus, would no longer be fortuitous; we should be able to make such modified viruses to order.

At present such things are largely a matter of speculation. But already chemically modified viruses have been made. The protein of tobacco mosaic virus has been altered by chemical treatment without destroying its ability to reproduce inside the living cells of the tobacco plant.

The significance of this chemical manipulation of viruses reaches far beyond the field of virus research. We can regard the virus as a piece of matter capable of reproducing itself. In this respect it behaves exactly like the chromosome matter of the living cell. The virus multiplying inside the cell is like an extra bit of living substance that has gate-crashed the chemical convention we describe as life.

By studying the behaviour of the virus we are studying, in effect, a piece of cell-substance that enjoys a regular spell of freedom from the normal activities of the cell. It is but a step from the chemical modification of the virus to the chemical modification of the genes and chromosomes which determine heredity characteristics in living things.

The process of mutation operates in the chromosomes of cell nuclei to produce variations in the offspring that derive from the cell. It seems reasonable to suppose, in view of what we now know about the chemistry of viruses, that mutation in living things is caused by chemical changes in the protein or nucleic acid constituents of chromosomes. Artificial modification of virus substances thus leads naturally to modification of the chemical constituents of the living cell.

It may be that we shall in this way find a solution to some of the great medical problems of the present time. Cancer, for example, is fundamentally a cell-reproduction that has run amok. In studying the reproduction process of the virus we may discover something that will lead us towards the control of the wild multiplication of cancer cells.

Knowledge of the chemistry that lies behind the processes of reproduction could, in this way, be of inestimable benefit to mankind. But, like all knowledge, it will bring its problems too. The ability to modify the chemical behaviour of cell-material will enable us to pre-select human personality in the test-tube. Let us hope that man's intelligence and social development is able to keep pace with the scientific progress that presents us with such a frightening responsibility.

18

Can we protect Ourselves?

In spite of all the wonder-drugs that we use so casually in medicine to-day, we still do not possess any chemical weapons that can be used effectively against the viruses that cause disease. Penicillin and 'Paludrine,' the sulpha drugs, streptomycin, and the rest are chemicals that can help us when the human body is invaded by 'ordinary' germs. But they can do little or nothing to prevent the multiplication of the viruses that cause so many of our most terrible diseases.

Some of the larger viruses are sensitive to drugs we use against bacteria. Penicillin, aureomycin, and other anti-biotics, for example, will prevent multiplication of the psittacosis virus and of the virus-like organism that causes typhus fever.

These large viruses, however, are now regarded as transitional organisms. They act as a link between the main group of viruses and the bacteria. They are viruses in that they will grow only inside a living cell; but they resemble bacteria in having some sort of organized body structure.

None of the true viruses are susceptible to the action of the antibiotics and synthetic drugs we use for treating bacterial diseases. Some of them will respond to heavy doses of drugs when they are growing in eggs or in tissue cultures. But the drugs have to be used in such large amounts that they would be too toxic for practical use.

The trouble with the virus is that it is not an independent, self-sufficient organism like a bacterium. It lives only in association with the cells in which it makes its home. It behaves in many ways like a little bit of cell-material, and cannot easily be distinguished chemically from a fragment of chromosome that has escaped from the nucleus of the cell.

This close similarity between the virus and the cell-material of its host is an embarrassment to the chemist who seeks a drug that can destroy the virus inside a living body. The drugs we use against disease bacteria are chemicals that can influence the living processes of the germ without causing undue harm to the body of the patient at the same time. Penicillin and the other antibiotic drugs, for example, can interfere with the chemical activities that make up the life of an ordinary germ, and they can do this without having any comparable effect on the living processes of the human body. This selectivity is possible because the disease bacterium is a distinct and different entity; it lives and multiplies without depending absolutely on living cells of its host for any of its vital needs. It can multiply, for example, on a simple food broth in a test tube.

It is reasonable to expect, therefore, that a chemical spanner can be thrown into the works of the bacterial cell without doing any simultaneous damage to the host-cells. This is what we do when we inject ourselves with drugs to cure a disease like pneumonia or septicæmia.

But it is obviously a different matter when we try to attack a virus in this way. Any chemical drug that is going to influence the multiplication of a virus is likely to affect the normal cell processes too. What is bad for the virus is probably going to be bad for the virus-like material of the cell.

In spite of the difficulties inherent in this chemical attack on viruses, we are not entirely helpless in our defence against these bits of delinquent cell substance. The virus may be very similar in structure to the material of the cell. But it is not exactly the same. If it was it could not alter the chemical programme of the cell's manufacturing processes. The nucleic acid and protein of the virus belong to the same chemical families as the nucleic acids and proteins of the cell. But the details of their hereditary character are different; and this means that the precise patterns of their chemical structures are different too.

In these chemical differences we have an opportunity— albeit a slight one—of carrying out a selective chemical attack against the virus. We can design a synthetic drug that would exploit the chemical differences that make the virus what it is.

There are three stages at which we can tackle the virus as it invades a living organism. We can attack it before it attaches itself to the prospective host-cell; we can prevent it making its entry into the cell; and we can stop it multiplying when it has gained access to the cell.

The natural defences of the animal body are based on the chemical mopping-up of viruses before they are able to invade the cell. When viruses enter the bloodstream the manufacture of special antibodies is stimulated. These antibodies are proteins which are designed specifically to neutralize the active chemical spots on the virus, preventing it from making its attack on the wall of a cell it would otherwise invade. Antibodies act like corks that impale themselves on the virus's chemical pin-points.

If we were in a position to make synthetic proteins to any specified design we could presumably make antibodies for use against any specific virus. By injecting these antibodies into our bloodstreams we could protect ourselves effectively against virus attack in its early stages. Unfortunately we are a long way from being able to manufacture synthetic antibodies, and there is little prospect of being able to do so for many years to come.

These antibodies, however, appear to act against the virus in a straightforward chemical way. The protein structure of the antibodies may indeed be much too complex for us to be able to reproduce it synthetically; but there is no reason why we should not make simpler substances that could have the same effect. As our understanding of the chemistry of virus behaviour deepens we should be able to devise and to manufacture chemical antibodies that will deal with the virus in the way that our antibodies do to-day.

Meanwhile we must content ourselves with our present methods of persuading the body to produce supplies of antibodies *in situ*. This we do by injecting either a harmless strain of virus, such as 17D in the case of yellow fever, or a virus that has been 'killed' by chemical treatment, as in the case of polio.

Work carried out in America during 1955 holds out great hopes that we shall be able to make this antibody-response much more effective in the future. Dr H. L. Fraenkel-Conrat and Dr Robley Williams, at the University of California, were able to separate the nucleic acid and protein of tobacco mosaic virus one from another. Each constituent, tested separately on tobacco plants, was non-infective. But on being brought together they recombined to make a complete, infective virus particle. This has been claimed as the first true synthesis of a living substance; two non-living chemicals were combined into a particle that could reproduce to form other particles in its image.

The protein of the tobacco mosaic virus was broken down during these experiments into doughnut-shaped fragments weighing about 400,000 times as much as a hydrogen atom. The long rods of true virus protein were apparently formed by the union of many of these sections; hollow rods of virus protein were produced, the hole down the middle being filled by a strand of nucleic acid when the two constituents were reunited.

These experiments were carried out in March 1955 and similar results were announced in August by Dr Barry Commoner and his colleagues at Washington University, St Louis.

The separation and recombination of virus into its constituents holds out hope of being able to produce 'hybrid' viruses by recombining fragments in different ways. Hybrids of this sort could be designed to stimulate antibody-production without causing actual disease. It is possible, also, that we could protect ourselves against the virus by using harmless fragments of it which would still retain the ability to stimulate antibody-production.

One difficulty inherent in this technique of persuading the body to mount its own attack on the virus is that it involves delay. Some days may elapse before the antibodies are being produced in sufficient quantity to be effective. We can, however, provide an immediate supply of antibodies by making use of those which other people have already manufactured. Antibodies are concentrated in the gamma globulin of the blood, and we can extract this from the blood donated by human volunteers. Injected into children, gamma globulin from adults who have been infected with measles, for example, will provide a ready-made supply of antibodies which can go into immediate action against any measles viruses.

The second point of chemical attack against the virus is during its attempt to enter the cell. This is a chemical process, and it can be countered by chemical methods. The use of RDE extracted from the cholera germ is a case in point;[1] this substance inactivates the sensitive patches on the cell-wall, so that the influenza virus has no way of getting inside the cell.

The penetration of some strains of bacteriophage into the bacterial cell can only take place if certain chemicals are available to the virus; without these chemicals the bacteriophage cannot carry out its chemical attack on the cell-wall. So, by making sure that the chemicals are not available to the virus, we can protect the bacterium from attack. There is a possibility that this sort of negative chemical technique may give us another method of protecting ourselves from virus disease.

The real answer to virus attack will come when we are

[1] See Chapter 15.

able to reach the virus inside the cell itself. If we can stop the virus multiplying without damaging the cell at the same time we shall be able to cure ourselves of virus diseases. But it is here, inside the cell, that the chemical similarity between the virus and the materials of the cell creates immense difficulties.

Under experimental conditions it has been possible to influence the multiplication of viruses inside their host-cells. Pneumonia viruses in mice and mumps viruses growing in fertile eggs will not multiply properly if the cells are provided with certain carbohydrates.

As yet we know insufficient about the chemical structure of the nucleic acids and proteins of animal viruses to be able to plan an effective chemical attack upon them. In the case of plant viruses we are on firmer ground; the chemical structures of a few nucleic acids and proteins of plant viruses are now understood in some detail. The design of virus nucleic acids, for example, is now known to differ in certain ways from the nucleic acids of the cells in which the virus multiplies. By making use of this knowledge we can influence the multiplication of the virus without having a corresponding effect on the self-duplicating processes of the cell itself.

A synthetic chemical called 8-azaguanine, sprayed on to a plant infected with tobacco mosaic virus, will take the place of a similar substance that the virus uses in building its nucleic acid. By incorporating 8-azaguanine in its nucleic acid the virus spoils the heredity blue-print that the chemical structure of its nucleic acid carries. Virus-production is thrown out of gear.

In the same way the multiplication of some bacterio-phages can be stopped by supplying them with chemicals that are similar to chemical units in their nucleic acid. Analysis of the nucleic acid manufactured by the virus has shown that the ' substitute ' chemical supplants as much as four-fifths of the usual one. So the pattern of the virus's nucleic acid is changed, and it becomes non-infective.

This chemical attack on the virus inside the cell is still in its early stages, and it is doubtful whether it can be put to practical use. Plants sprayed with 8-azaguanine, for example, convert this chemical rapidly into other substances. It is difficult to maintain sufficient of the 8-azaguanine in the plant to cope with invading viruses.

Also the 8-azaguanine goes into the nucleic acid of the plant cells too; it can damage the growth of the cells as well as that of the virus. This drawback may be less serious than it sounds; the production of nucleic acid by the virus is so rapid that it could well use up most of the substitute chemical before the cell has a chance to start using it.

Many human and animal viruses have been allowed to multiply in the presence of 8-azaguanine, but the chemical has had no inhibiting effect. Experiments have shown, however, that 8-azaguanine finds its way into the nucleic acid of tumour cells in mice and some other animals.

As we learn more about the detailed chemical structure of the nucleic acids of viruses we may be able to find substitutes for chemical units that are exclusive to the virus. We know already that some bacterial viruses contain units which are not present in the nucleic acid of the bacteria they attack. If we can provide the viruses with substitute chemicals that can take the place of these units we may be able to block the multiplication of viruses without affecting the reproduction of cell nucleic acid at all.

It is with this in mind that virus researchers are studying the chemical design of virus nucleic acids. So far only one or two have been analysed in real detail; there are hundreds of virus nucleic acids of which we still know nothing at all.

This shortage of vital information is characteristic of most aspects of virus research. Everything we discover about the virus creates new problems of its own; the more we find out, the more there is left to find out.

In its way this virus research is much more important to us than all the atomic energy projects that occupy so much of our scientists' time to-day. The virus is leading us towards an understanding of the processes of life itself; virus research could banish the last of man's terrible diseases from the earth, and give us control over the processes of heredity that are the basis of human personality.

It is characteristic of our strange modern world that we should spend thousands of millions of pounds on harnessing atomic energy, and yet leave virus research to a few enthusiastic scientists often working on university budgets.

It is a tribute to their wonderful work that virus research has already taken us so far. What a prospect awaits us when we can provide them with the encouragement they deserve!

Index